THE
NIKOLA TESLA
PUZZLE
COLLECTION

M

METRO BOOKS
New York

An Imprint of Sterling Publishing Co., Inc.
1166 Avenue of the Americas
New York, NY 10036

Design and artwork © 2015 Carlton Books Ltd

ISBN 978-1-4351-6221-1

For information about custom editions, special sales, and premium and corporate purchases,
please contact Sterling Special Sales at 800-805-5489 or specialsales@sterlingpublishing.com.

Manufactured in Dubai

3 5 7 9 1 0 8 6 4

www.sterlingpublishing.com

The copyright holder would like to thank Corbis, Dover Books, Getty Images, Istockphoto.com,
Mary Evans Picture Library, Shutterstock.com & Topfoto.co.uk for their kind permission
to reproduce the photographs and illustrations in this book.

THE NIKOLA TESLA PUZZLE COLLECTION

AN ELECTRIFYING SERIES OF CHALLENGES, ENIGMAS AND PUZZLES

Richard Galland

METRO BOOKS
New York

CONTENTS

Introduction 10

Born in a Storm.........................14

Complete the Grid I 15

Faith, Hope and Clarity 16

Sequence I..................................19

Stone Age Pioneers 20

Value System I...........................22

Power Grid I..............................23

Town Planning I........................24

Watery Grave.............................26

Complete the Grid II...............27

Visions.......................................28

Pattern Recognition I 31

Future Power.............................32

Watch Your Eight.....................36

Complete the Grid III 37

Familiarity 38

Value System II 39

Sequence II 40

Power Grid II 41

Complete the Grid IV...............42

Value System III.......................43

Peace of Mind...........................44

Fill in Your Name.....................47

It's Alive!....................................48

The $50,000 Joke 50

Complete the Grid V 51

Power Supply I 52

Imposter 54

Value System IV 55

Town Planning II 56

Power Grid III...........................58

Lost in the Grid 59

Complete the Grid VI 60

Frequency I 61

Power Supply II 62

The Madman of Harlem 63

Vive La France 66

Smugglers 69

Science vs Catastrophe 70

Power Grid IV 72

Complete the Grid VII 73

Value System V 74

Power Supply III 75

Research 76

Handy 77

Bagels 78

Complete the Grid VIII 79

New World 80

50 Death Dealers 84

Complete the Grid IX 86

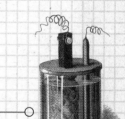

Sequence III.............................87

Value System VI 88

Power Supply IV........................89

Marathon...................................90

Power Grid V 91

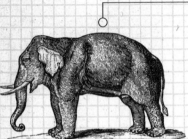

War of the Currents 92

Power Supply V 95

Multidisciplinary 96

Complete the Grid X................98

Value System VII......................99

Predators.................................100

Pattern Recognition II............101

Teleforce.................................102

Complete the Grid XI............103

Power Grid VI........................104

Frequency II............................105

Electric City...........................106

Chaos 108

Complete the Grid XII..........111

Facing Facts 112

Value System VIII 113

Break In 114

Town Planning III...................116

Watt Did They Say?.................118

Complete the Grid XIII..........119

Technical Support....................120

Life Force..............................122

Shopping 125

Complete the Grid XIV..........126

Value System IX.....................127

Hardwire 128

Complete the Grid XV 129

Power Supply VI......................130

Hidden Genius 131

Space Race.............................132

Power Grid VII 136

Pattern Recognition III 137

Feathered Friends....................138

Complete the Grid XVI..........141

Town Planning IV...................142

Value System X.......................144

Mark Twain............................145

Power Supply VII....................146

Tower of Dreams....................147

Complete the Grid XVII........148

Town Planning V 150

Complete the Grid XVIII.......152

Swing Batter 153

Pattern Recognition IV...........154

Science Conference..................155

Solutions................................156

INTRODUCTION

Electrical power is something we now take for granted; with the touch of a button electrons flow and the devices we have come to depend on are brought to life.

But it wasn't until the latter part of the 19th century that an explosion of innovations in electrical engineering and radio wave transmission would lead to our era of worldwide communication. These innovations were pioneered by many great minds, some of whom remain in relative obscurity while others have become household names.

The Alternating Current (AC) that brings light and other essential comforts to our homes owes much to the work of a visionary genius named Nikola Tesla.

Tesla's story is replete with impossible ambition, incredible breakthroughs and no small amount of personal tragedy. Like many talented men who dream of a better tomorrow, he found himself at odds with and exploited by the world of commerce. Tesla's ideas were both ridiculed and appropriated by his rivals, and he died in poverty.

The rivalry between Tesla and Thomas Edison – known as the War of the Currents – has become a topic of much fascination in recent years. Tesla is hailed by some as a heroic victim and Edison painted by others as a profiteering villain; it's unlikely that the truth is that simple...

Technology requires both dreamers and doers; it would be fair to say that both men deserve recognition.

Tesla's legacy is enduring and can be seen in technology as diverse as neon lighting, X-rays and wireless communication. One ambition he did not fulfil in his lifetime was the creation of unlimited wireless power, but advances have been made in recent years that might one day realize this dream.

When we consider the mind of a man like Tesla we often ask ourselves – was he a natural-born genius or did his upbringing play a part? From an early age his parents encouraged him to exercise and develop his mental faculties. The book you are holding is designed to do the same; it is a collection of puzzles, many of which are themed around Tesla's life and work. You'll find a variety of conundrums to test your logic, memory, observation and even lateral thinking. I hope you enjoy it and – who knows – maybe you'll discover your inner genius too.

"The human being is a self-propelled automaton entirely under the control of external influences. Willful and predetermined though they appear, his actions are governed not from within, but from without. He is like a float tossed about by the waves of a turbulent sea."

NIKOLA TESLA

BORN IN A STORM

Nikola Tesla was born at the stroke of midnight, July 10 1856, in the village of Smiljan, which lies on the eastern edge of Austria-Hungary (now Croatia).

His mother, Georgina Đuka, was a skilled weaver and a talented inventor in her own right; Milutin, his father, was a priest.

A violent electrical storm raged overhead as Tesla came into the world, an appropriate portent for a child who would become the 'Master of Lightning'.

Let your mind be like lightning now and answer this question quickly:

There are 31 days in July. But how many months have 28 days?

SOLUTION ON PAGE 158

COMPLETE THE
GRID 1

What should go in the black square to complete the grid?

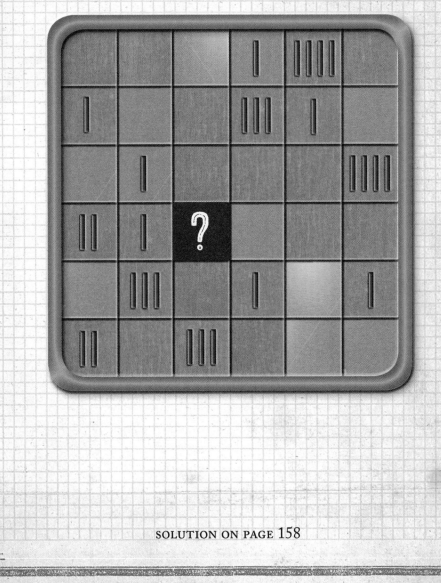

SOLUTION ON PAGE 158

FAITH, HOPE & CLARITY

Milutin Tesla expected his son to join him in the clergy, but Nikola contracted cholera before he could join the seminary. Lying on his sick bed close to death, the young genius begged his father to let him study engineering instead of theology. Milutin agreed, Nikola made a dramatic recovery and his place in history was assured.

On the next page you can see a variety of images. Take a couple of minutes to picture them in your mind and then turn over the page…

> "Let the future tell the truth, and evaluate each one according to his work and accomplishments. The present is theirs; the future, for which I have really worked, is mine."
>
> **NIKOLA TESLA**

SOLUTION ON PAGE 159

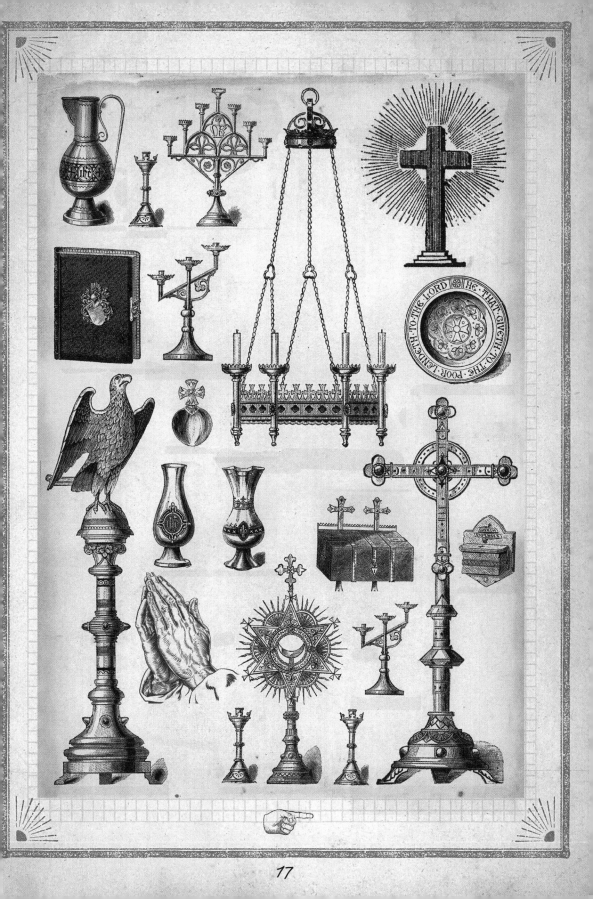

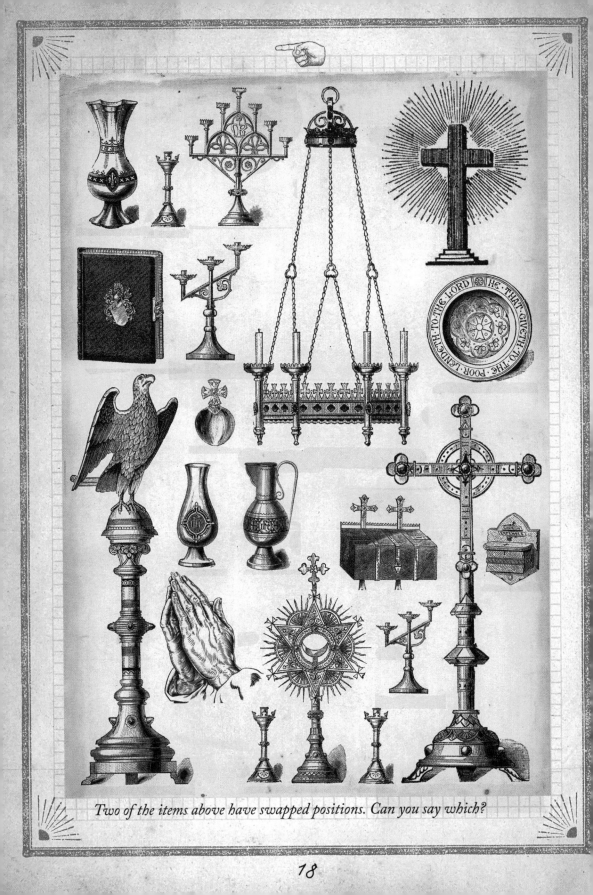

Two of the items above have swapped positions. Can you say which?

SEQUENCE I

Complete the sequence below.

F	S	T	F
F	S	S	E
N	T	E	T
T	F	F	?

SOLUTION ON PAGE 160

STONE AGE PIONEERS

Some of humanity's greatest inventions predate recorded history. Just for fun let's find out who invented what, what inspired their discovery and how they were rewarded by their tribe.

1. The caveman who was banished from his tribe after eating some strange mushrooms was neither Nigel nor the inventor of fire.

2. Stig's invention of the plough was not inspired by a storm and neither was the inventor who was worshipped as a god.

3. The inventor of the bow was made chief of his tribe.

4. Neither Ugg, nor the inventor of the bow, nor the caveman who went hunting, had a monument built in their honour.

	Invention	Inspiration	Reward
Zog			
Ugg			
Stig			
Nigel			

SOLUTION ON PAGE 161

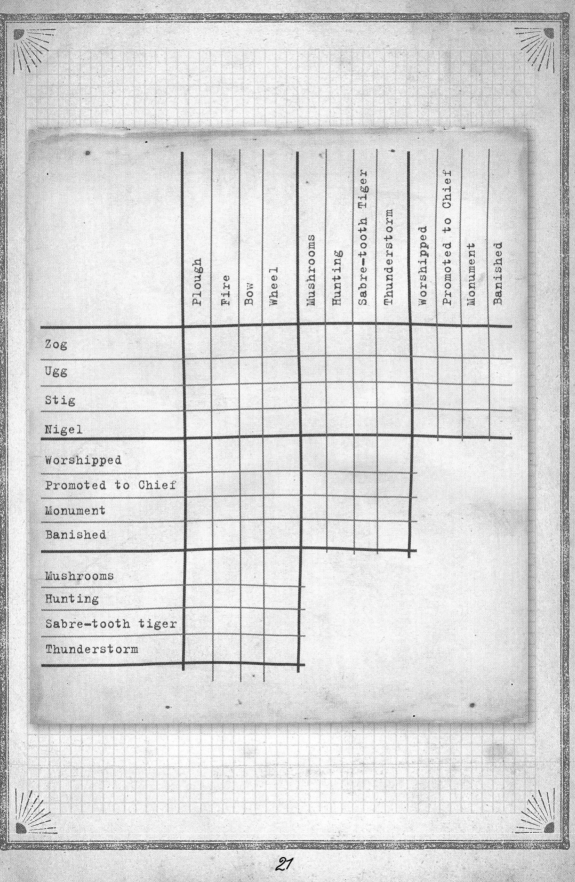

	Plough	Fire	Bow	Wheel	Mushrooms	Hunting	Sabre-tooth Tiger	Thunderstorm	Worshipped	Promoted to Chief	Monument	Banished
Zog												
Ugg												
Stig												
Nigel												
Worshipped												
Promoted to Chief												
Monument												
Banished												
Mushrooms												
Hunting												
Sabre-tooth tiger												
Thunderstorm												

VALUE SYSTEM I

Work out the value of each component to determine what number replaces the question mark.

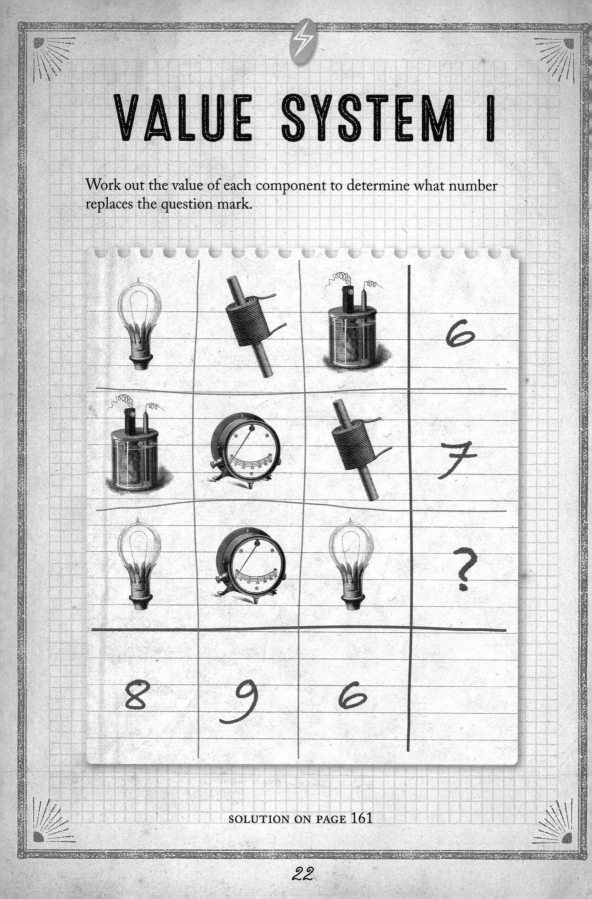

POWER GRID I

1. Run a single, unbroken wire around the grid that passes through each of the relays to complete the circuit.

2. The wire must enter and leave each square through the centre of one of its four sides.

3. If the wire enters a gold relay, it must immediately turn 90 degrees left or right on that square. It must also pass straight through the square it came from and the square it leads to.

4. If the wire enters a silver relay, it must pass straight through the square. It must also turn left or right in the next and/or preceding square.

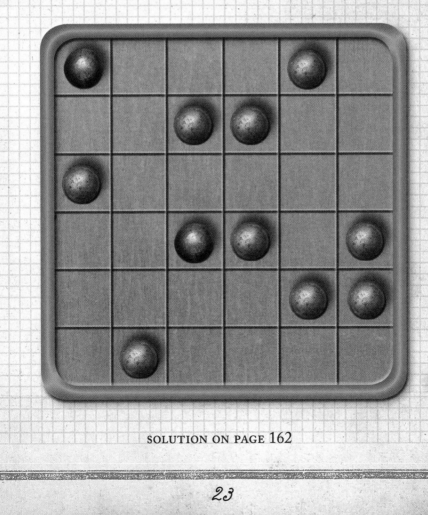

SOLUTION ON PAGE 162

TOWN PLANNING I

Congratulations on your appointment as Chief of Town Planning. Your city is divided into six districts. The mayor has decreed that each district shall have one each of the following facilities:

🏠 Housing   🏭 Factory   🏙 Offices

🏛 School   🏟 Stadium   🌲 Park

You must make sure that there is no more than one of each facility in each column and row, and that no facilities of the same type are adjacent to one another.

SOLUTION ON PAGE 163

WATERY GRAVE

The bodies of three men were found in three separate rooms. Each room was full of water and nothing else.

The coroner reported that each of the men died of different causes, but in each case it was as a direct result of being in the water.

Only one of the men drowned. So how did the other two die?

SOLUTION ON PAGE 164

COMPLETE THE GRID II

What should go in the black square to complete the grid?

SOLUTION ON PAGE 164

VISIONS

It was clear from an early age that Tesla's mind worked on a different frequency; he was given to vivid waking dreams that he could barely distinguish from reality. His inspiration for hydro-electric power apparently came from a vision of a wheel being turned by the Niagara Falls. In 1896 this dream would become a reality and usher in the Electronic Age.

On the opposite page you can see a variety of images.
Take a couple of minutes to picture them in your mind and then turn over the page…

"Today's scientists have substituted mathematics for experiments, and they wander off through equation after equation, and eventually build a structure which has no relation to reality."

NIKOLA TESLA

SOLUTION ON PAGE 165

Four of the items above have changed positions. Can you say which?

PATTERN RECOGNITION I

1   2   4

7   ?

Which of the shapes below completes the sequence?

11   11   9   9

A   B   C   D

SOLUTION ON PAGE 166

FUTURE POWER

Young scientists from the nation's most distinguished universities have entered a competition to solve the world's energy crisis. Can you match the inventor to their university, and work out which source of energy they discovered and how many gigawatts of power they were able to produce?

1. Henry Hawking was able to harvest sufficient quantities of anti-matter to fuel his generator.

2. Princeton's brightest young mind, Tina Tesla, did not harness the power of Earth's gravity.

3. The University of Berkeley regretted not having Eleanor Einstein on its team after her discovery generated an impressive 250 gigawatts.

4. The idea for converting human emotions into energy originated at Harvard. The inventor had developed the idea after splitting up with his girlfriend.

5. Norbert Newton's invention generated more than 100 gigawatts but not as many as the inventor who converted tachyons (particles of time) into a sustainable source of energy.

Scientist	University	Source	Output
Eleanor Einstein			
Henry Hawking			
Tina Tesla			
Norbert Newton			

SOLUTION ON PAGE 166

	Berkeley	MIT	Princeton	Harvard	Emotions	Tachyons	Gravity	Anti-matter	100 gigawatts	150 gigawatts	250 gigawatts	300 gigawatts
Eleanor Einstein												
Henry Hawking												
Tina Tesla												
Norbert Newton												
100 gigawatts												
150 gigawatts												
250 gigawatts												
300 gigawatts												
Emotions												
Tachyons												
Gravity												
Anti-matter												

"Every living being is an engine geared to the wheelwork of the universe. Though seemingly affected only by its immediate surroundings, the sphere of external influence extends to infinite distance."

NIKOLA TESLA

WATCH YOUR EIGHT

Without writing anything down can you say how many times the number 8 occurs in the number sequence 1 to 100?

8

88

888

8888

SOLUTION ON PAGE 167

COMPLETE THE GRID III

What should go in the black square to complete the grid?

SOLUTION ON PAGE 167

FAMILIARITY

Clara and Betty had come to hear the last will and testament of the late electrical tycoon, Sir Avery Shorte-Fuse.

Just as the proceedings were about to begin, the doors burst open and a young woman entered the room.

Neither Clara nor Betty had ever set eyes on the woman before, yet both angrily exclaimed, "Oh drat, it's Diane!"

Can you explain how they could recognize the stranger and why they would react so negatively?

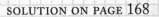

SOLUTION ON PAGE 168

VALUE SYSTEM II

Work out the value of each component to determine what number replaces the question mark.

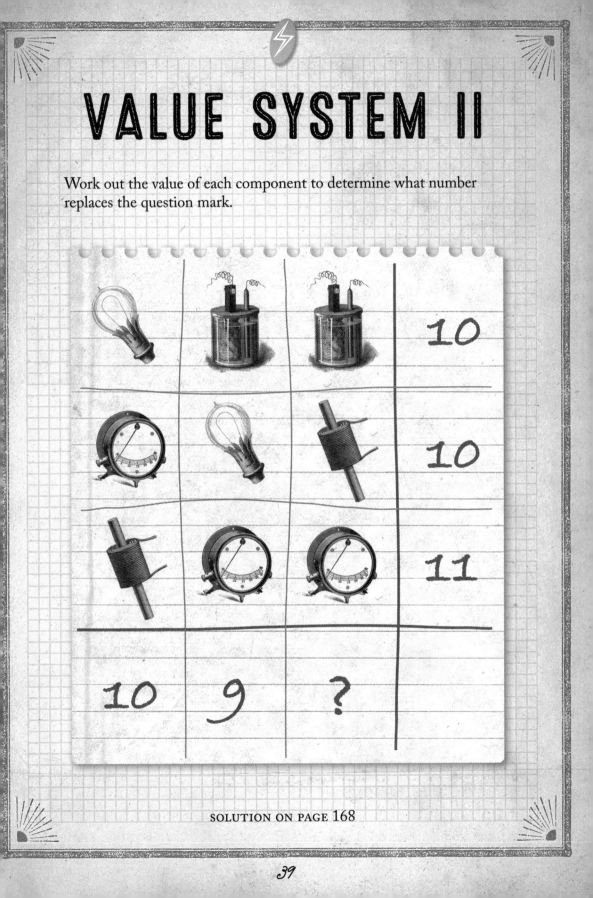

SOLUTION ON PAGE 168

SEQUENCE II

What is the missing number?

SOLUTION ON PAGE 169

POWER GRID II

1. Run a single, unbroken wire around the grid that passes through each of the relays to complete the circuit.

2. The wire must enter and leave each square through the centre of one of its four sides.

3. If the wire enters a gold relay, it must immediately turn 90 degrees left or right on that square. It must also pass straight through the square it came from and the square it leads to.

4. If the wire enters a silver relay, it must pass straight through the square. It must also turn left or right in the next and/or preceding square.

SOLUTION ON PAGE 170

COMPLETE THE GRID IV

What belongs in the empty box?

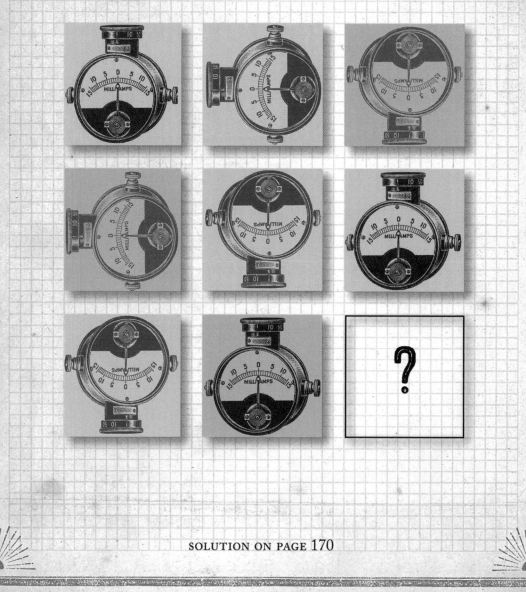

SOLUTION ON PAGE 170

VALUE SYSTEM III

Work out the value of each component to determine what number replaces the question mark.

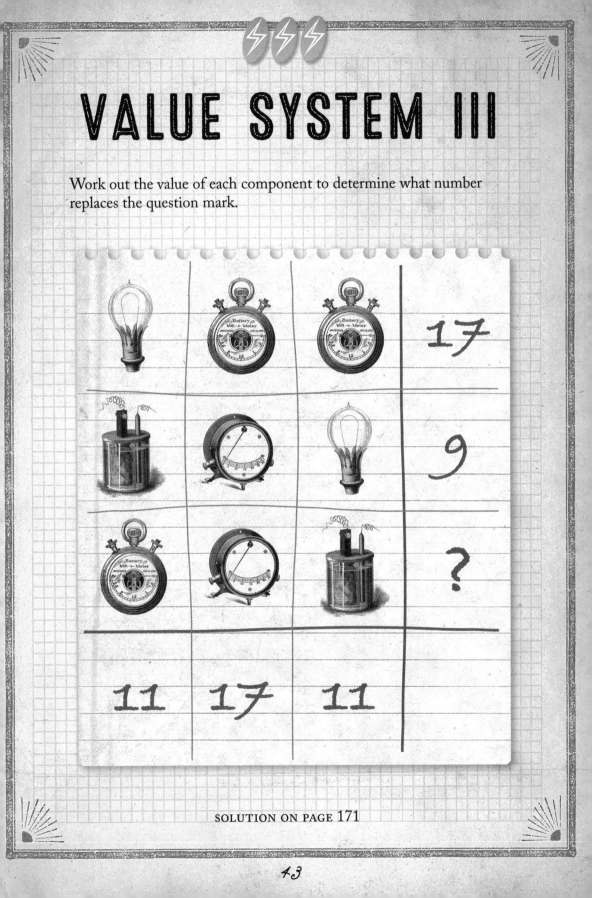

PEACE OF MIND

Tesla was a paradoxical man. A committed humanitarian who abhorred violence, he dodged the draft in 1874. However, some of his later inventions included ideas for a devastating 'doomsday weapon'.

On the opposite page you can see a variety of images. Take a couple of minutes to picture them in your mind and then turn over the page…

"Our virtues and our failings are inseparable, like force and matter. When they separate, man is no more."

NIKOLA TESLA

SOLUTION ON PAGE 172

Four of the items above have swapped positions. Can you say which?

FILL IN YOUR NAME

Can you insert the letters T, E, S, L and A into the grid below so that no letter is repeated on the same row, column or diagonal?

IT'S ALIVE!

Using electricity to reanimate dead tissue was once considered a scientific possibility. Four lonely scientists have decided to create "golems" from assorted body parts. Can you say where each professor created his golem, the name he gave it and what happened?

1. Professor Knutz moved to a disreputable neighbourhood in Berlin to conduct his experiments.

2. The whole of New York City suffered a power outage when the golem called "Bob" was brought to life. Unsurprisingly the disgruntled citizens did not make him a national hero.

3. Not all of the golems were monstrous; one professor thought his golem was so lovely, he stayed in Paris and married it.

4. Professor Phreekdoubt suffered an existential crisis after talking to his golem and ended up in therapy; he did not name his creation "Bob."

5. The wealthy professor Bankenstein named his golem "Jerry."

6. The golem called "Ron" was not made in London.

Professor	Location	Golem	Outcome
Van der Volt			
Bankenstein			
Knutz			
Phreekdoubt			

	New York	London	Paris	Berlin	Ron	Phil	Jerry	Bob	Got married	Bloody rampage	Therapy	National hero
Van der Volt												
Bankenstein												
Knutz												
Phreekdoubt												
Got married												
Bloody rampage												
Therapy												
National hero												
Ron												
Phil												
Jerry												
Bob												

SOLUTION ON PAGE 173

THE $50,000 JOKE

In 1884 Edison told Tesla he would pay him $50,000 if he could improve his Direct Current generators. Tesla worked night and day to accomplish the task and succeeded, but his request for payment was met with derision: "Tesla, you don't understand our American humour!" said the ungrateful Edison.

It was 3am and Tesla was wide awake. Suddenly he rushed from his room all the way to Edison's door. He began knocking furiously until his employer appeared.

The two men engaged in a short, heated exchange then Tesla turned on his heel, made his way back to his residence and fell asleep within minutes.

Can you explain Tesla's behaviour?

SOLUTION ON PAGE 174

COMPLETE THE
GRID V

What belongs in the empty box?

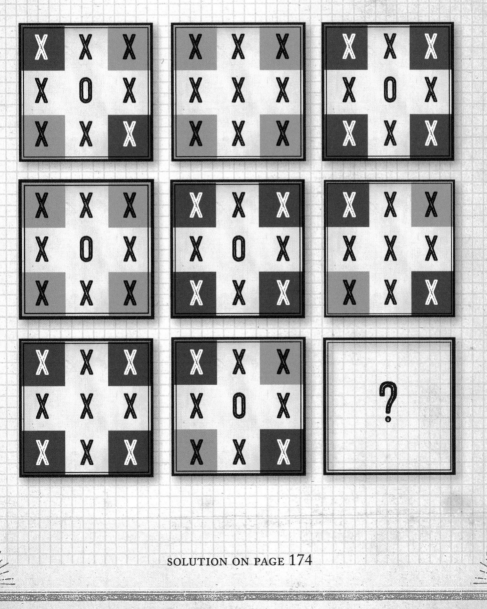

SOLUTION ON PAGE 174

POWER SUPPLY I

1. Place a battery (⚡) in a square adjacent to each lightbulb on the grid.

2. Adjacent squares share a side (north, south, east and west) not just a corner.

3. No lightning bolt can be placed adjacent to another battery.

4. The numbers tell you how many batteries must be placed in each row or column.

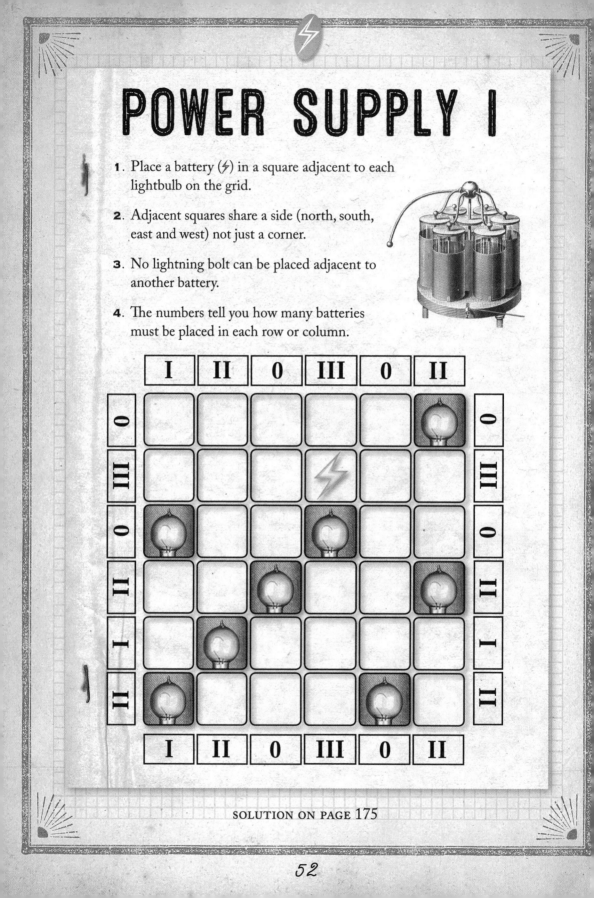

	I	II	0	III	0	II	
0						💡	0
III				⚡			III
0	💡			💡			0
II			💡			💡	II
I		💡					I
II	💡				💡		II
	I	II	0	III	0	II	

SOLUTION ON PAGE 175

" It seems that I have always been
ahead of my time. I had to wait
19 years before Niagara was harnessed
by my system, 15 years before
the basic inventions for wireless,
which I gave to the world in 1893,
were applied universally. "

NIKOLA TESLA

IMPOSTER

Agent Hardy had been sent on a mission to rescue the particle physicist Doctor Jefferson who claimed to have perfected Tesla's "Deathray".

When she arrived at his lab, she was alarmed to find not one but two identical Doctor Jeffersons.

"He's an impostor!" the two lab-coated men shouted simultaneously.

The quick thinking agent covered both men with her gun and found two syringes in a drawer.

"I'm taking you both back with me," she said, "but I want a sample of your blood for analysis, right now."

The "Jefferson" on her left took a syringe and nervously rolled up his sleeve. The one to her right shook his head and backed away.

Agent Hardy's gun barked, wounding the left-hand Jefferson in the leg before he even applied the syringe.

"Let's go," she said to the other.

Can you explain her actions?

SOLUTION ON PAGE 175

VALUE SYSTEM IV

Work out the value of each component to determine what number replaces the question mark.

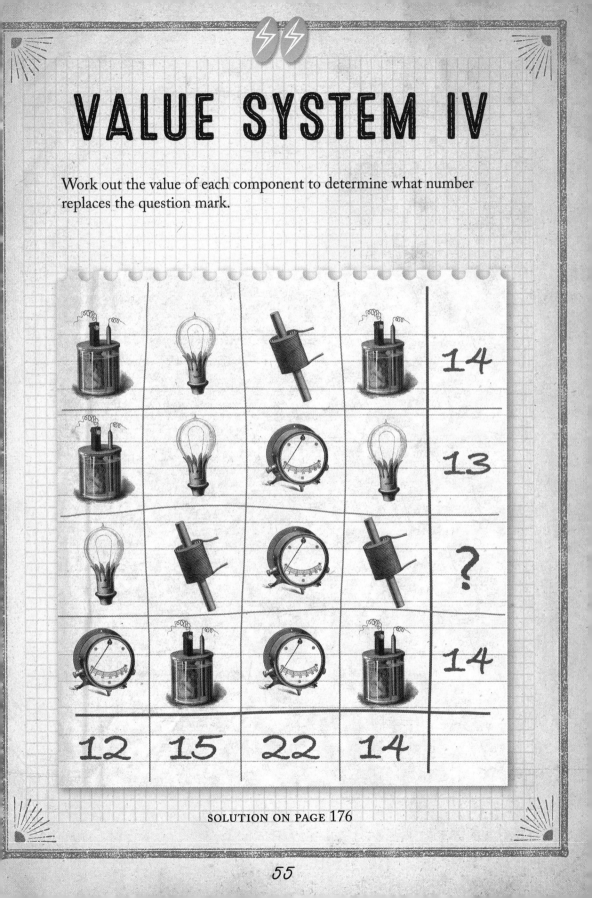

TOWN PLANNING II

Your city is divided into six districts. The mayor has decreed that each district shall have one of each of the following facilities:

🏘 Housing   🏭 Factory   🏢 Offices

🏛 School   🏟 Stadium   🌲 Park

You must make sure that there is no more than one of each facility in each column and row, and that no facilities of the same type are adjacent to one another.

SOLUTION ON PAGE 176

POWER GRID III

1. Run a single, unbroken wire around the grid that passes through each of the relays to complete the circuit.

2. The wire must enter and leave each square through the centre of one of its four sides.

3. If the wire enters a gold relay, it must immediately turn 90 degrees left or right on that square. It must also pass straight through the square it came from and the square it leads to.

4. If the wire enters a silver relay, it must pass straight through the square. It must also turn left or right in the next and/or preceding square.

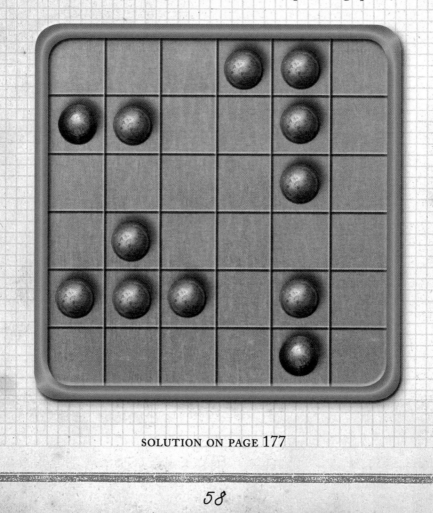

SOLUTION ON PAGE 177

LOST IN THE GRID

The name TESLA can only be found once in the grid below, reading up, down, forwards, backwards and diagonally. Can you find it?

L	S	L	L	T	S	S	L	A	E	E	T	S	S	L	A	L	A
T	A	S	L	E	S	L	T	S	S	L	A	T	S	L	T	T	S
A	L	L	T	S	E	A	S	S	T	A	L	L	E	L	E	E	S
S	S	A	S	E	S	L	R	L	E	T	E	L	T	T	E	S	E
S	L	S	L	S	A	T	E	A	E	E	S	L	A	T	L	S	A
L	L	L	A	T	E	S	A	T	L	S	T	A	L	L	A	A	T
S	T	S	S	E	S	L	S	T	S	L	E	S	T	S	S	L	A
T	E	S	L	E	A	S	L	A	E	E	E	T	E	S	L	T	S
S	S	E	A	L	A	S	T	S	S	L	L	S	S	E	A	S	S
A	T	S	L	A	S	L	S	S	T	A	T	A	T	S	L	S	T
L	S	T	E	S	A	L	S	T	A	S	A	L	S	T	E	L	L
S	L	E	T	T	E	S	A	E	E	T	S	S	L	E	T	E	S
L	T	E	E	A	S	L	E	S	T	E	S	L	T	E	E	S	T
T	S	S	L	A	S	S	L	A	E	S	E	A	S	S	S	E	A
E	S	L	T	S	S	L	T	S	S	T	S	S	L	A	T	S	L
S	E	A	S	S	T	A	L	L	A	E	S	L	T	L	L	T	E
T	S	S	L	A	E	S	T	S	S	E	S	L	T	S	L	E	T
E	S	L	T	S	E	T	E	S	L	S	E	A	S	L	T	E	E

SOLUTION ON PAGE 178

COMPLETE THE GRID VI

What belongs in the empty box?

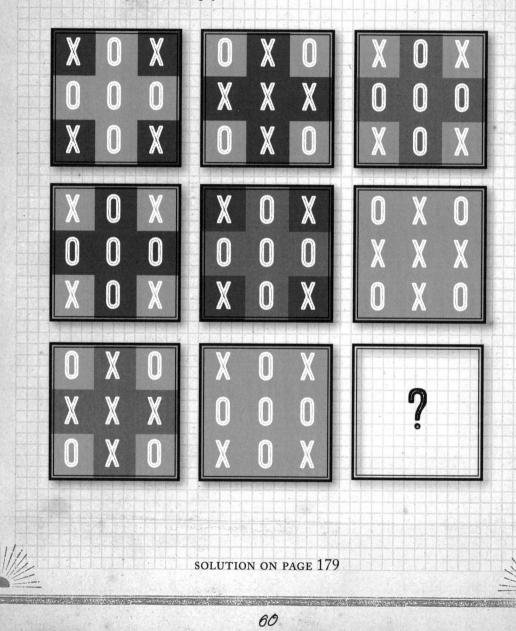

SOLUTION ON PAGE 179

FREQUENCY 1

Can you identify these four pioneers of science and technology just from the frequency of letters in their names?

1

A	B	C	D	E	F	G	H	I	J	K	L	M
2	0	1	0	1	0	0	0	1	0	0	0	0

N	O	P	Q	R	S	T	U	V	W	X	Y	Z
2	1	0	0	0	1	1	0	0	1	0	0	0

2

A	B	C	D	E	F	G	H	I	J	K	L	M
1	1	0	0	3	0	0	0	2	0	0	1	0

N	O	P	Q	R	S	T	U	V	W	X	Y	Z
2	0	0	0	1	1	2	0	0	0	0	0	0

3

A	B	C	D	E	F	G	H	I	J	K	L	M
4	0	1	1	1	1	0	1	1	0	0	1	1

N	O	P	Q	R	S	T	U	V	W	X	Y	Z
0	0	0	0	1	0	0	0	0	0	0	1	0

4

A	B	C	D	E	F	G	H	I	J	K	L	M
2	0	0	0	1	0	0	0	1	0	1	2	0

N	O	P	Q	R	S	T	U	V	W	X	Y	Z
1	1	0	0	0	1	1	0	0	0	0	0	0

SOLUTION ON PAGE 179

POWER SUPPLY II

1. Place a battery (⚡) in a square adjacent to each lightbulb on the grid.

2. Adjacent squares share a side (north, south, east and west) not just a corner.

3. No lightning bolt can be placed adjacent to another battery.

4. The numbers tell you how many batteries must be placed in each row or column.

SOLUTION ON PAGE 180

62

THE MADMAN OF HARLEM

Walking through Upper Manhattan with his archrival, Tesla pointed to an unkempt man with an impressive beard.

"They call him Nicholas Nickelbeard," said Tesla. *"If you offer him a choice between a nickel and a dime, he'll always take the nickel."*

"That's baloney," scoffed Edison; *"no one could be that stupid."*

"Find out for yourself," said Tesla.

So Edison approached the man and produced a dime in one hand and a nickel in the other.

"Which would you like?" he smirked.

"The nickel, please, sir," replied Nicholas Nickelbeard, cheerfully taking the proffered five cents.

"That is seriously the dumbest schmuck I've ever met," said Edison when they were out of earshot.

"I very much doubt it," said Tesla with a smile.

Can you explain?

SOLUTION ON PAGE 180

"If we want to reduce poverty and misery, if we want to give to every deserving individual what is needed for a safe existence of an intelligent being, we want to provide more machinery, more power. Power is our mainstay, the primary source of our many-sided energies."

NIKOLA TESLA

VIVE LA FRANCE

In 1882 Tesla moved to France and began work at Continental Edison where he improved electrical equipment.

On the opposite page you can see a variety of images. Take a couple of minutes to picture them in your mind and then turn over the page...

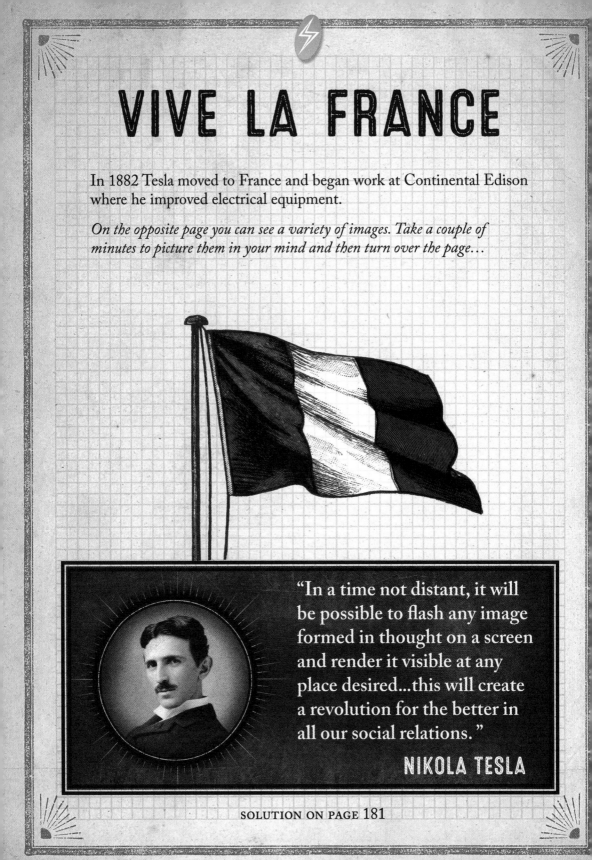

"In a time not distant, it will be possible to flash any image formed in thought on a screen and render it visible at any place desired...this will create a revolution for the better in all our social relations."

NIKOLA TESLA

SOLUTION ON PAGE 181

Two of the items above have swapped positions. Can you say which?

SMUGGLERS

A notorious gang who were suspected of smuggling stolen goods was under surveillance. Each time they entered the country, they were searched from head to toe, their trunks and glove compartments unlocked and the contents scrutinized, their clothes, even their bodies, were probed and X-rayed, but the authorities could find nothing.

However it was widely rumoured that the gang's fortune was getting bigger with each trip. So what were they up to?

SOLUTION ON PAGE 182

SCIENCE VS CATASTROPHE

Four (quite mad) scientists are working hard to save the world from impending doom.

Can you say which scientist is a specialist in which field, the nature of catastrophe he predicts and what solution he proposes?

1. Harry Stottle was not the astrophysics professor who proposed building a fleet of spacecraft and moving to Mars to avoid the catastrophe.

2. Ty Neilson believed that living underground was our only hope, whereas the professor who predicted an imminent Ice Age thought we could only survive with the help of robot servants.

3. Palaeontologist Gary Leo was adamant that the greatest threat did not come from outer space.

4. At a press conference the eminent geologist stated, "Our planet is under attack from extra-terrestrial aliens!" Professor Dorkins said, "There is absolutely no danger of a meteor strike."

5. The marine biologist did not think accelerated genetic mutation could save us from disaster.

Professor	Field	Catastrophe	Solution
Dick Dorkins			
Ty Neilson			
Harry Stottle			
Gary Leo			

	Geology	Astrophysics	Palaeontology	Marine Biology	Global flood	Alien invasion	Ice Age	Meteor strike	Genetic mutation	Robot servants	Live underground	Move to Mars
Dick Dorkins												
Ty Neilson												
Harry Stottle												
Gary Leo												
Genetic mutation												
Robot servants												
Live underground												
Move to Mars												
Global flood												
Alien invasion												
Ice Age												
Meteor strike												

SOLUTION ON PAGE 182

POWER GRID IV

1. Run a single, unbroken wire around the grid that passes through each of the relays to complete the circuit.

2. The wire must enter and leave each square through the centre of one of its four sides.

3. If the wire enters a gold relay, it must immediately turn 90 degrees left or right on that square. It must also pass straight through the square it came from and the square it leads to.

4. If the wire enters a silver relay, it must pass straight through the square. It must also turn left or right in the next and/or preceding square.

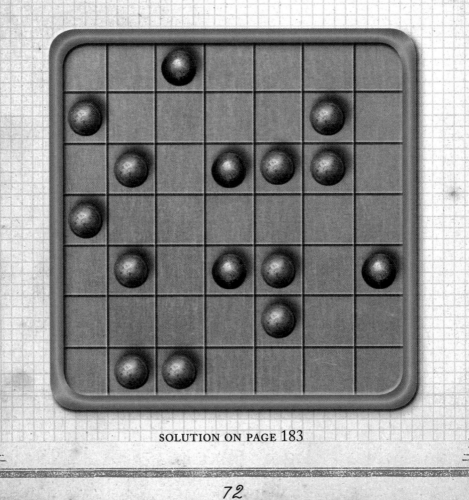

SOLUTION ON PAGE 183

COMPLETE THE GRID VII

What belongs in the empty box?

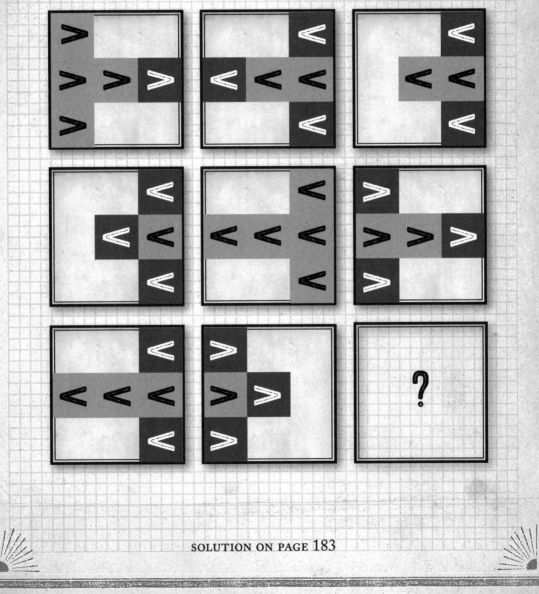

SOLUTION ON PAGE 183

VALUE SYSTEM V

Work out the value of each component to determine what number replaces the question mark.

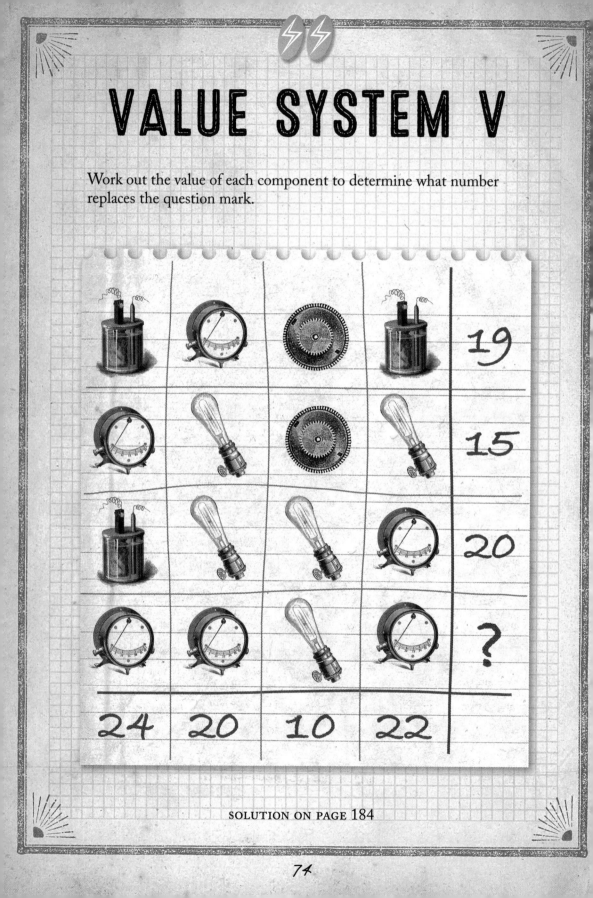

POWER SUPPLY III

1. Place a battery (⚡) in a square adjacent to each lightbulb on the grid.

2. Adjacent squares share a side (north, south, east and west) not just a corner.

3. No battery can be placed adjacent to another battery.

4. The numbers tell you how many batteries must be placed in each row or column.

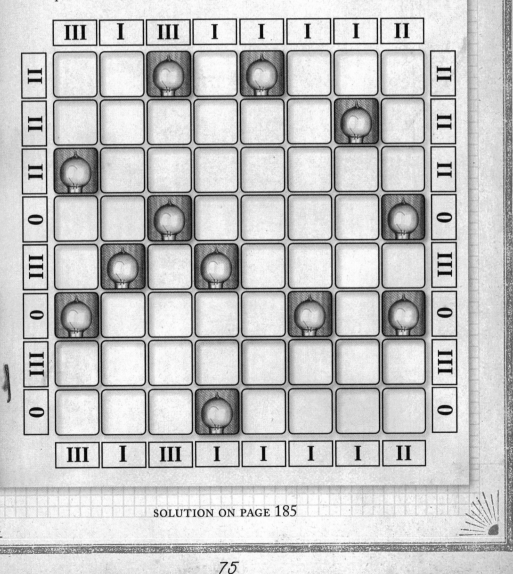

SOLUTION ON PAGE 185

RESEARCH

Three types of specialist are working on a project.

The biochemists are always 100% truthful.

The statisticians are always 100% untruthful.

The accountants are able to make whatever they say true.

The director selects 18 researchers and assigns them to three teams of six.

Alpha Team consists of specialists all of the same type.

Bravo Team has an even split of two types of specialist.

Charlie Team has an even split of all three types.

Unfortunately the network crashes on the first day and team details are lost. The director faces three teams but has no way of knowing which team is which.

Team 1 says: "All our members are biochemists."

Team 2 says: "All our members are statisticians."

Team 3 says: "All our members are accountants."

The director decides that she needs to drop the mendacious statisticians. But how many people must she fire?

SOLUTION ON PAGE 186

HANDY

Tesla was enjoying a meal at an exclusive restaurant with his friend Mark Twain. The drink was flowing freely and the clientele were celebrating rather noisily.

"How the wealthy love to flaunt their vulgarity," said Tesla, "it's like a circus freak show."

Twain smiled at his friend's snobbery and said with mock alarm, "Don't turn around, but there's a man at the table yonder who has five hands."

Tesla rolled his eyes and continued to eat, knowing how Twain's mind worked.

What had Mark Twain seen?

SOLUTION ON PAGE 187

BAGELS

Each morning the bagel seller buys his bagels at two cents each then sets off to make his deliveries. He arrives at Tesla's lab at midday and sells his last bagel for one dollar fifty.

"You must be making a fortune," remarked Tesla.

"Not even close," said the bagel seller miserably, *"you're my one and only customer."*

On his way to Tesla's lab the bagel seller must travel through the territories of three notorious street gangs. In each territory he is forced to pay a tariff of half of the bagels he is carrying, plus two more, to the gang leader.

So does the bagel seller make a profit at all?

SOLUTION ON PAGE 187

COMPLETE THE GRID VIII

What belongs in the empty box?

NEW WORLD

In 1884, after an eventful voyage, Tesla arrived in the United States with just four cents and a letter of recommendation in his pocket. But he had a head full of ideas and a determination to live the American Dream.

On the next page you can see a variety of images. Take a couple of minutes to picture them in your mind and then turn over the page…

> "In the twenty-first century, the robot will take the place which slave labour occupied in ancient civilization."
>
> **NIKOLA TESLA**

SOLUTION ON PAGE 189

Two of the items above have swapped positions. Can you say which?

> We wind a simple ring of iron with coils; we establish the connections to the generator, and with wonder and delight we note the effects of strange forces which we bring into play, which allow us to transform, to transmit and direct energy at will.

NIKOLA TESLA

DEATH DEALERS

Tesla's secret blueprints for a teleforce "Death Ray" have been stolen and are now available on the black market to the highest bidder. Some of the world's most ruthless criminal organizations are eager to get their hands on the weapon and threaten to use it on national landmarks.

Can you match the prospective buyer to their intended target, their motive and their bid for the Death Ray?

1. The Yakuza, who did not bid $666 million, were not the power crazed organization that targeted Big Ben.

2. The Triads placed the highest bid for the Death Ray. The lowest bid did not come from the buyer who just wanted to blow stuff up for fun.

3. The Cartels thought the Sistine Chapel would make a suitable target. The Mafia intended to use the weapon to even the score in an ongoing vendetta.

4. The blackmailers hoped to extort enough money to make a profit on their $250 million bid and didn't think threatening the Eiffel Tower would raise that sort of money.

Buyer	Target	Motive	Bid
Mafia			
Yakuza			
Triads			
Cartels			

SOLUTION ON PAGE 190

	The White House	Big Ben	Sistine Chapel	The Eiffel Tower	Power	Blackmail	Fun	Vendetta	$100 million	$250 million	$666 million	$901 million
Mafia												
Yakuza												
Triads												
Cartels												
$100 million												
$250 million												
$666 million												
$901 million												
Power												
Blackmail												
Fun												
Vendetta												

COMPLETE THE GRID IX

What belongs in the empty box?

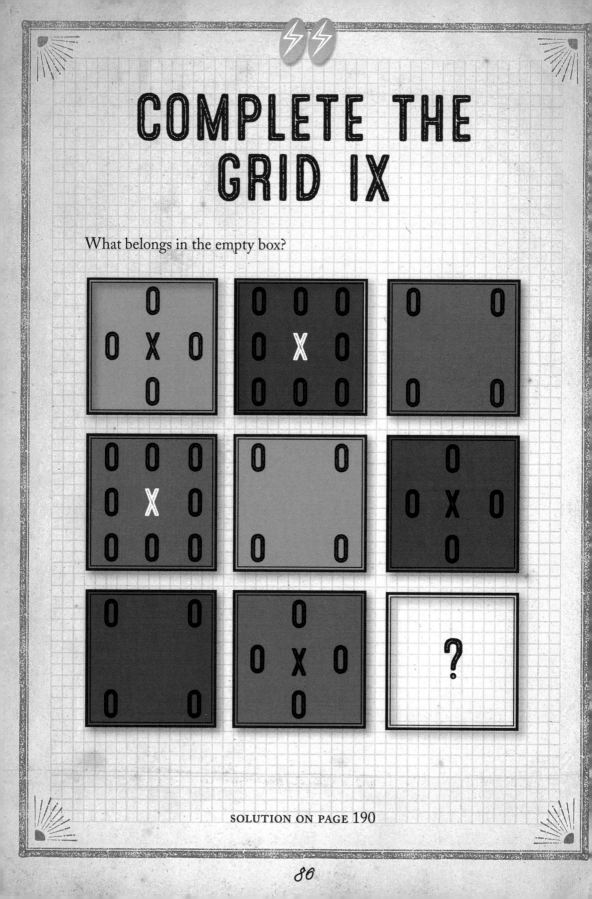

SEQUENCE III

What is the missing number?

TWO	FOUR	SIX	EIGHT	TEN
2	11	20	22	?

SOLUTION ON PAGE 191

VALUE SYSTEM VI

Work out the value of each component to determine what number replaces the question mark.

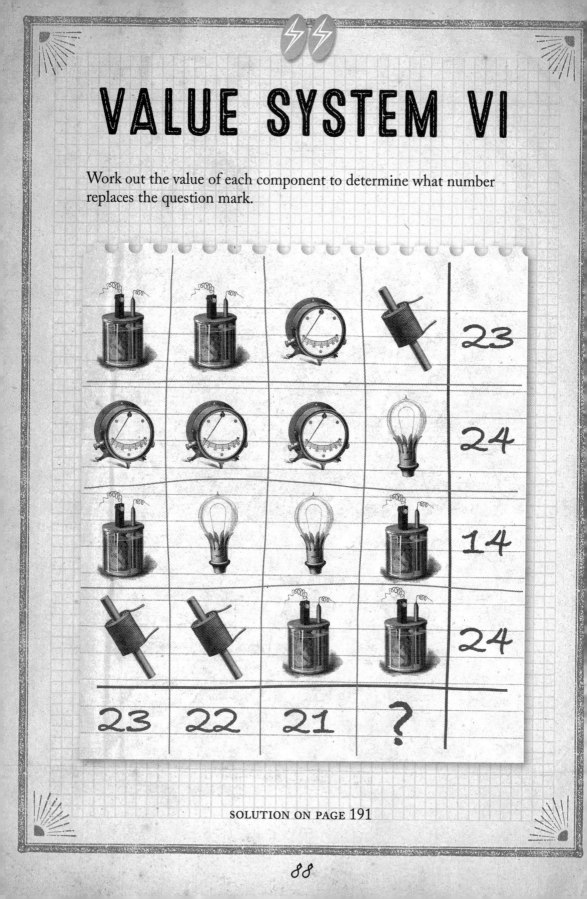

SOLUTION ON PAGE 191

POWER SUPPLY IV

1. Place a battery (⚡) in a square adjacent to each lightbulb on the grid.

2. Adjacent squares share a side (north, south, east and west) not just a corner.

3. No battery can be placed adjacent to another battery.

4. The numbers tell you how many batteries must be placed in each row or column.

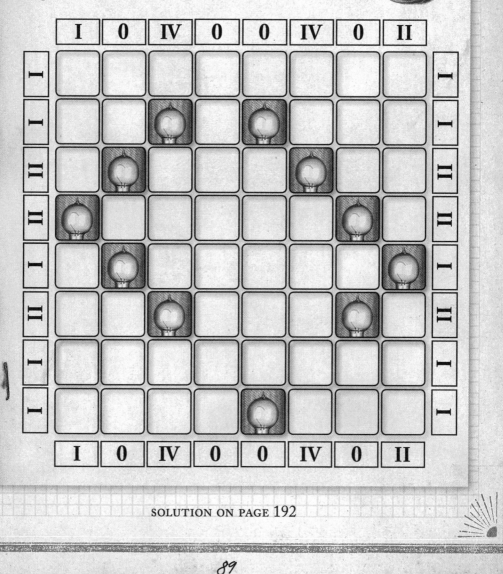

	I	0	IV	0	0	IV	0	II	
I									I
I			💡		💡				I
III		💡				💡			III
III	💡						💡		III
I		💡					💡		I
III			💡				💡		III
I									I
I				💡					I
	I	0	IV	0	0	IV	0	II	

SOLUTION ON PAGE 192

MARATHON

Jack is a gifted athlete who has trained hard for the Olympic marathon. In the last hundred yards he finds the inner strength to increase his pace and overtakes the runner in second place.

But then, with the finishing line just feet away, he is overtaken by two other runners…

What medal will Jack receive?

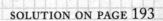

SOLUTION ON PAGE 193

POWER GRID V

1. Run a single, unbroken wire around the grid that passes through each of the relays to complete the circuit.

2. The wire must enter and leave each square through the centre of one of its four sides.

3. If the wire enters a gold relay, it must immediately turn 90 degrees left or right on that square. It must also pass straight through the square it came from and the square it leads to.

4. If the wire enters a silver relay, it must pass straight through the square. It must also turn left or right in the next and/or preceding square.

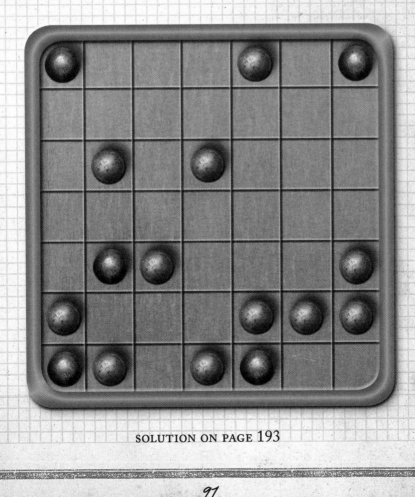

SOLUTION ON PAGE 193

WAR OF THE CURRENTS

It has been reported that in his efforts to discredit Tesla and his Alternating Current, Edison put on some grisly demonstrations, including publicly electrocuting an elephant with AC. This may not be true, although Edison and Tesla were indeed fierce rivals.

On the opposite page you can see a variety of images. Take a couple of minutes to picture them in your mind and then turn over the page…

"Electrical science has revealed to us the true nature of light, has provided us with innumerable appliances and instruments of precision, and has thereby vastly added to the exactness of our knowledge."

NIKOLA TESLA

SOLUTION ON PAGE 194

Two of the items above have swapped positions. Can you say which?

POWER SUPPLY V

1. Place a battery (⚡) in a square adjacent to each lightbulb on the grid.

2. Adjacent squares share a side (north, south, east and west) not just a corner.

3. No battery can be placed adjacent to another battery.

4. The numbers tell you how many batteries must be placed in each row or column.

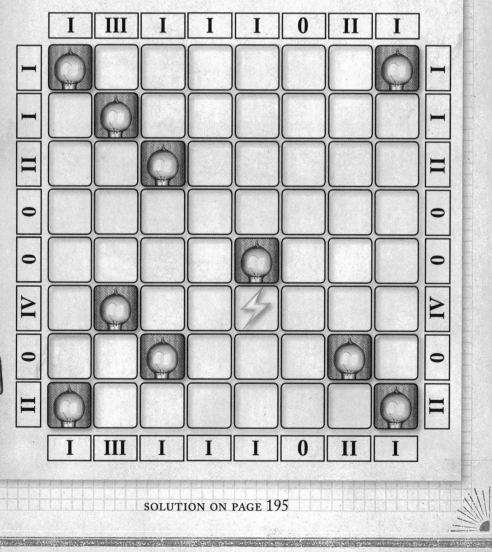

SOLUTION ON PAGE 195

MULTI-DISCIPLINARY

Professor Grohl, Professor Dickinson and Professor Hendrix are all multitalented; each of them specializes in four fields. There are two specialists assigned to each of the six fields listed in the table opposite.

Using your powers of logical deduction can you work out who specializes in what from the statements?

If Grohl specializes in zoology then he also understands psychology

If Grohl specializes in psychology then he doesn't understand chemistry

If Grohl specializes in chemistry then he doesn't understand geology

If Hendrix specializes in mathematics then she doesn't understand zoology

If Hendrix specializes in zoology then she also understands geology

If Hendrix specializes in geology then she also understands chemistry

If Dickinson specializes in chemistry then she also understands geology

If Dickinson specializes in geology then she doesn't understand zoology

If Dickinson specializes in zoology then she doesn't understand mathematics

	GROHL	HENDRIX	DICKINSON
CHEMISTRY			
GEOLOGY			
ZOOLOGY			
MATHEMATICS			
PSYCHOLOGY			
ASTRONOMY			

SOLUTION ON PAGE 196

COMPLETE THE GRID X

What belongs in the empty box?

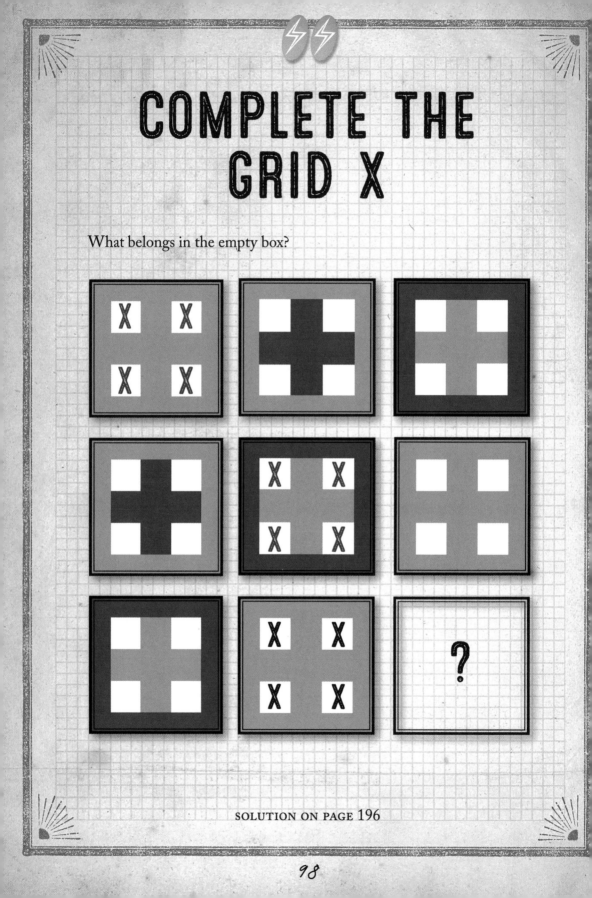

VALUE SYSTEM VII

Work out the value of each component to determine what number replaces the question mark.

SOLUTION ON PAGE 197

PREDATORS

"The business world is a jungle," said Edison condescendingly; "there are wolves that'll dog your every step waiting for you to slip up, leeches that'll suck you dry and hyenas that'll strip the assets from your rotting carcass."

"A nice zoological metaphor, particularly given your love of elephants," said Tesla dryly. "And I suppose you're the king of the jungle?"

"Damned right I am."

"King of a group that will swallow you whole if you don't swallow it first." said Tesla.

"Huh?" said Edison.

SOLUTION ON PAGE 197

PATTERN RECOGNITION II

Which of the shapes below completes the sequence?

A   B   C   D

SOLUTION ON PAGE 198

TELEFORCE

Tesla has constructed two prototypes for his "Death Ray" tower.

Tower A can fire a beam of energy five times in five seconds, Tower B can fire ten times in ten seconds.

Assuming that he starts his watch when the first shot is fired, which tower can fire 12 beams in the shorter time?

"There is no memory or retentive faculty based on lasting impression. What we designate as memory is but increased responsiveness to repeated stimuli."

NIKOLA TESLA

SOLUTION ON PAGE 198

COMPLETE THE GRID XI

What belongs in the empty box?

SOLUTION ON PAGE 199

POWER GRID VI

1. Run a single, unbroken wire around the grid that passes through each of the relays to complete the circuit.

2. The wire must enter and leave each square through the centre of one of its four sides.

3. If the wire enters a gold relay, it must immediately turn 90 degrees left or right on that square. It must also pass straight through the square it came from and the square it leads to.

4. If the wire enters a silver relay, it must pass straight through the square. It must also turn left or right in the next and/or preceding square.

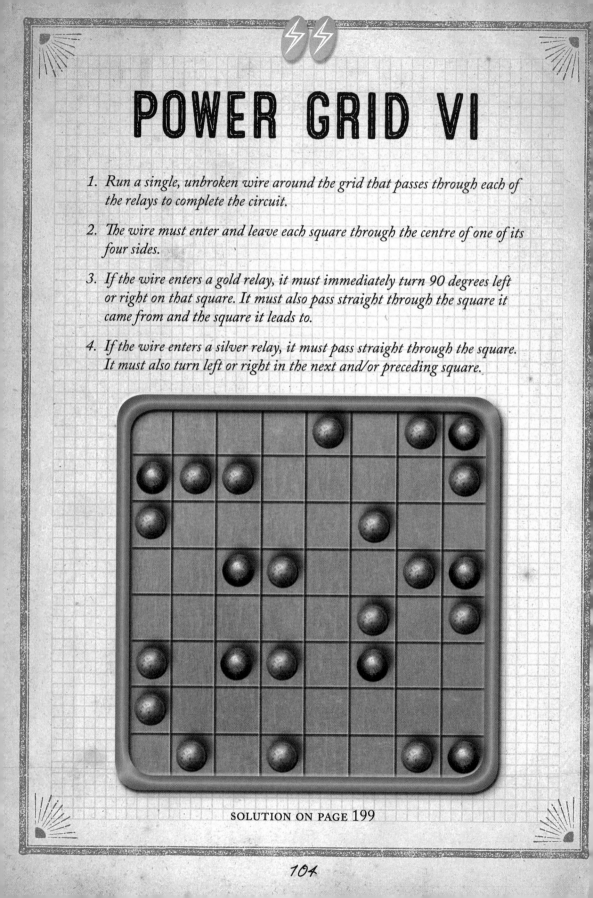

SOLUTION ON PAGE 199

FREQUENCY II

Can you identify these four pioneers of science and technology just from the frequency of letters in their names?

1

A	B	C	D	E	F	G	H	I	J	K	L	M
2	0	1	2	1	0	0	0	2	0	0	1	0

N	O	P	Q	R	S	T	U	V	W	X	Y	Z
2	2	0	0	1	0	0	0	1	0	0	0	0

2

A	B	C	D	E	F	G	H	I	J	K	L	M
2	1	0	0	1	1	0	0	2	1	1	1	1

N	O	P	Q	R	S	T	U	V	W	X	Y	Z
4	0	0	0	1	0	0	0	0	0	0	0	0

3

A	B	C	D	E	F	G	H	I	J	K	L	M
1	0	0	1	1	0	0	1	1	0	0	0	1

N	O	P	Q	R	S	T	U	V	W	X	Y	Z
1	2	0	0	0	2	1	0	0	0	0	0	0

4

A	B	C	D	E	F	G	H	I	J	K	L	M
3	1	1	0	1	0	0	0	1	0	0	2	0

N	O	P	Q	R	S	T	U	V	W	X	Y	Z
0	0	1	0	0	2	0	0	0	0	0	0	0

SOLUTION ON PAGE 200

ELECTRIC CITY

The awards for the most Innovative City will soon be announced. Can you work out the order of the prize winners, the city, the name of its mayor and its unique innovation?

1. The spaceport in Jackson connected Mississippi with the rest of the known universe.

2. Payne, who wasn't Mayor of Seattle, and Mayor Tomlinson, whose city could control its own weather, finished with one prize-winning city between them.

3. The third prize went to Mayor Styles' city which was located on the east coast.

4. The city with the zero gravity sports arena took the second prize; it wasn't Miami.

	Prize	City	Mayor	Innovation
First				
Second				
Third				
Fourth				

SOLUTION ON PAGE 200

	Miami	Seattle	Jackson	Boston	Styles	Tomlinson	Horan	Payne	Spaceport	Weather control	Undersea dome	Zero gravity arena
First Prize												
Second Prize												
Third Prize												
Fourth Prize												
Spaceport												
Weather control												
Undersea dome												
Zero gravity arena												
Styles												
Tomlinson												
Horan												
Payne												

CHAOS

In 1895, while Tesla was still mourning the death of his mother, further disaster struck. A fire tore through his New York workshop leaving all his work in ashes.

On the opposite page you can see a variety of images. Take a couple of minutes to picture them in your mind and then turn over the page…

"Archimedes was my ideal. I admired the works of artists, but to my mind, they were only shadows and semblances. The inventor, I thought, gives to the world creations which are palpable, which live and work."

NIKOLA TESLA

Write down everything you can remember from the previous page – no peeking!

1	
2	
3	
4	
5	
6	
7	
8	
9	
10	
11	
12	
13	
14	
15	
16	
17	
18	
19	
20	

COMPLETE THE
GRID XII

What belongs in the empty box?

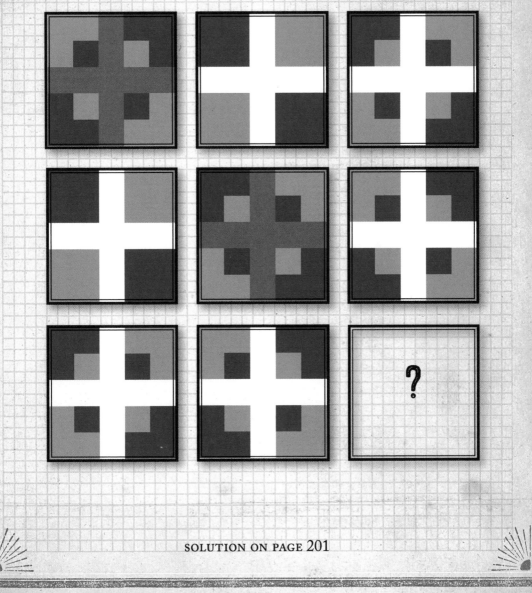

SOLUTION ON PAGE 201

FACING FACTS

Three competitive chemists Alice, Brigitte and Carly have been working on an anti-aging tonic. Each of them takes a vial of their own formula and drinks…

Within a few minutes the face of each scientist has turned an alarming shade of green!

All three burst into fits of laughter at the ridiculous state of the other two.

But Alice stops immediately when she realizes that her own face must have changed colour.

Can you explain how she came to this conclusion?

SOLUTION ON PAGE 201

VALUE SYSTEM VIII

Work out the value of each component to determine what number replaces the question mark.

BREAK IN

Some people were envious of Tesla's work. But to what lengths would they go to bring him down?

One night two men broke into Tesla's lab. One took an axe to the door of his workshop and made a quick search of the room before leaving the place in utter chaos.

When Tesla returned to the building, he found his entire life's work in ruins. The two intruders were standing nearby, only feet away from a police officer. Tesla was certain that the men had broken into his lab, but he did not press charges.

Why?

SOLUTION ON PAGE 202

> " The scientists of today think deeply instead of clearly. One must be sane to think clearly, but one can think deeply and be quite insane. "

NIKOLA TESLA

TOWN PLANNING III

Your city is divided into six districts. The mayor has decreed that each district shall have one of each of the following facilities:

🏘 Housing 🏭 Factory 🏙 Offices
🏛 School 🏟 Stadium 🌲 Park

You must make sure that there is no more than one of each facility in each column and row, and that no facilities of the same type are adjacent to one another.

SOLUTION ON PAGE 203

WATT DID THEY SAY?

Three young electrical engineers are working on portable generators for Edison Inc. They each make three claims about their generator's power, two of which are true and one false.

Alfred: "My machine generated 3600 watts."

Bart: "Well, at least mine wasn't the lowest output."

Charlie: "My output was less than Alfred's."

Alfred: "My output was 800 watts less than Bart's."

Bart: "There was a 1200 watt difference between mine and Charlie's."

Charlie: "Bart generated 1200 watts more than Alfred."

Alfred: "I generated 400 watts more than Charlie."

Bart: "Charlie's output was 4800 watts."

Charlie: "Alfred generated 4000 watts."

Can you work out the output of each generator?

SOLUTION ON PAGE 203

COMPLETE THE GRID XIII

What belongs in the empty box?

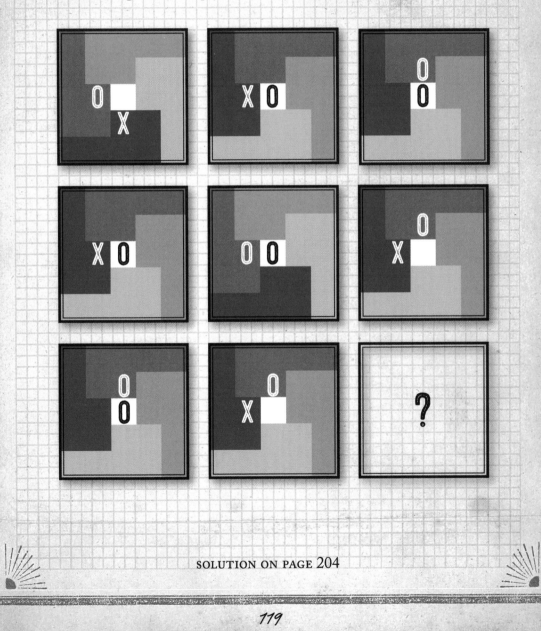

SOLUTION ON PAGE 204

TECHNICAL SUPPORT

Four network users have contacted technical support to report problems. Can you match the user to their email account; discover their password and the nature of their problem?

The user who accessed their hatemail account with the password ICU812 has the same numbers in their username as the user who lost their files.

Sux2Bme is the positivity-deficient password of user CB1.

The user who had no network connection to access their ickipedia email has a longer username than the person with the most self-evident password.

SnOOp doesn't use hatemail but his system got a nasty virus.

Username	Email	Password	Problem
CB1			
PlgPen			
SnOOpee			
WOOdstck			

	@ickypedia.org	@hatemail.net	@gargle.com	@yaaboo.com	Sux2Bme	password	ICU812	12345	Power outage	No network	Lost files	Virus
CB1												
PlgPen												
Sn00pee												
W00dstck												
Power outage												
No network												
Lost files												
Virus												
Sux2Bme												
password												
ICU812												
12345												

SOLUTION ON PAGE 204

LIFE FORCE

After losing his life's work, Tesla's life spiralled into madness. He developed an interest in Indian mysticism and became a disciple of the chemist, and mystic, Sir William Crookes and even began using electricity on himself.

On the opposite page you can see a variety of images. Take a couple of minutes to picture them in your mind and then turn over the page…

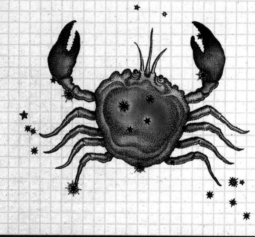

"The scientific man does not aim at an immediate result. His work is like that of the planter – for the future. His duty is to lay the foundation for those who are to come, and point the way."

NIKOLA TESLA

SOLUTION ON PAGE 205

Two of the items above have swapped positions. Can you say which?

SHOPPING

Tesla went to his local hardware store.

"You can have one for five dollars or five for ten," said the owner.

"That wouldn't be much use," said Tesla; "how much for six?"

"I see what you mean. Well, six is 15 dollars, and I can do nine for – "

"That's fine; I think I'll just take 12."

"That will be 20 dollars, please."

What is Tesla buying?

SOLUTION ON PAGE 206

COMPLETE THE GRID XIV

What belongs in the empty box?

SOLUTION ON PAGE 206

VALUE SYSTEM IX

Work out the value of each component to determine what number replaces the question mark.

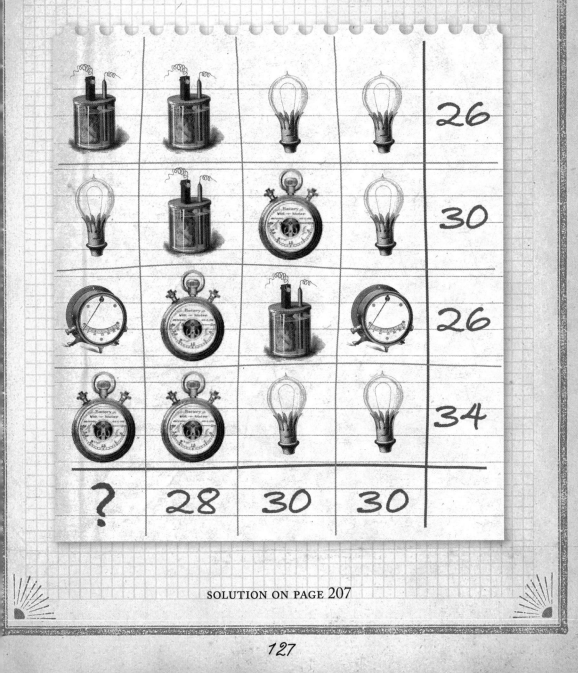

SOLUTION ON PAGE 207

HARDWIRE

Tesla has been wiring up his new workshop. He has three identical wires which run from the basement to his lab on the top floor. The wires had been tagged at both ends. Unfortunately, after the wires have been run through the building he finds that the labels (A, B and C) he attached to the top floor wires have fallen off.

He has a machine that will show if a current is passing through a wire but only if both ends of the wire are attached to the machine. How many trips downstairs must he make to determine which wire is which?

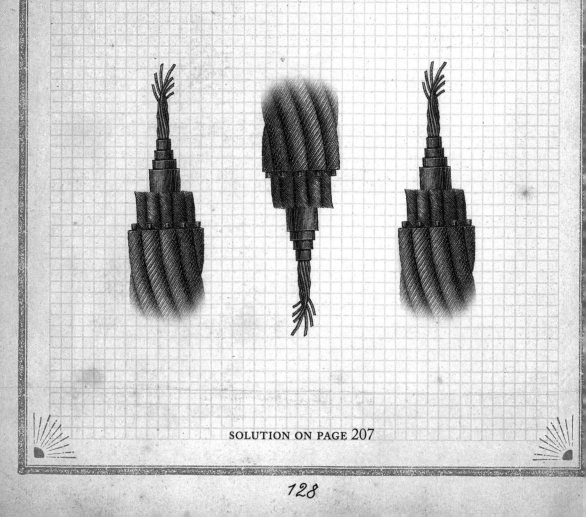

SOLUTION ON PAGE 207

COMPLETE THE GRID XV

What belongs in the empty box?

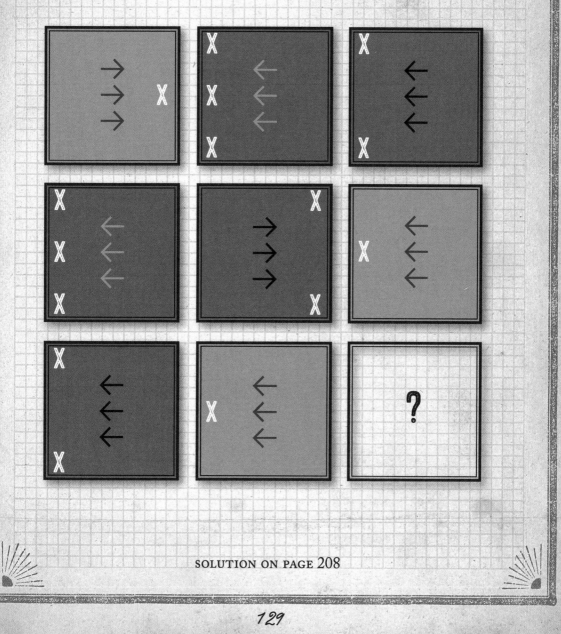

SOLUTION ON PAGE 208

POWER SUPPLY · VI

1. Place a battery (⚡) in a square adjacent to each lightbulb on the grid.

2. Adjacent squares share a side (north, south, east and west) not just a corner.

3. No battery can be placed adjacent to another battery.

4. The numbers tell you how many batteries must be placed in each row or column.

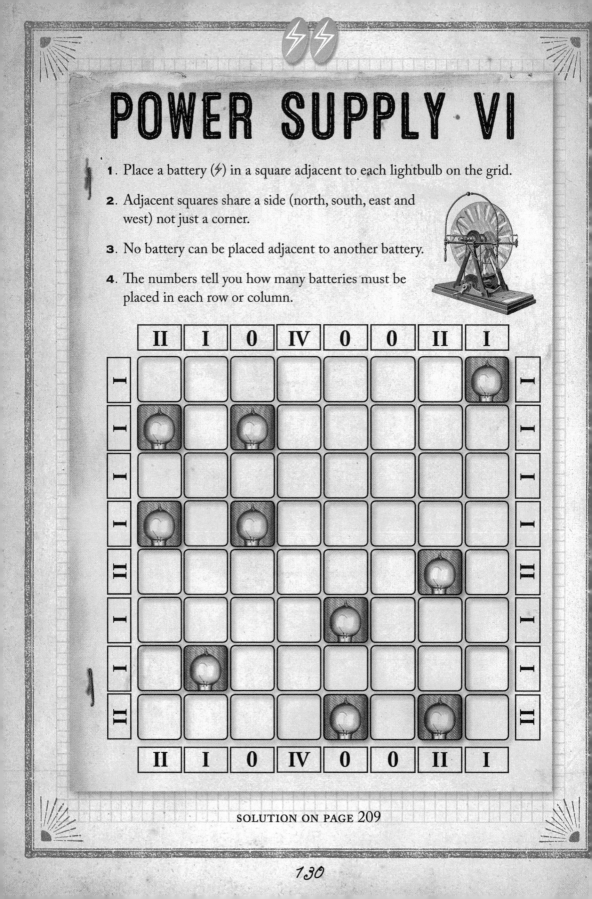

HIDDEN GENIUS

How many great minds do you know?

How many of them can you find in this grid?

N	I	E	T	S	N	E	G	T	T	I	W	A	L	O	A	G	A
O	C	A	O	A	E	K	A	D	I	P	U	I	M	Y	V	V	O	A
R	I	T	Z	I	C	N	M	I	J	E	H	F	A	G	G	Y	S
A	Y	B	W	D	E	Y	A	W	A	C	E	V	U	S	A	A	R
W	S	A	P	G	E	A	L	S	E	T	K	A	Z	E	L	C	D
D	I	N	A	C	A	O	O	I	A	O	G	A	D	F	I	G	E
A	Q	E	S	A	V	H	L	Z	E	N	E	L	E	A	L	O	T
A	T	C	C	O	B	J	Z	E	E	L	C	Q	S	F	E	E	D
S	R	A	A	K	O	C	A	E	G	T	V	U	Y	A	O	U	A
A	G	Z	L	O	H	H	P	L	W	N	U	O	R	S	O	E	R
V	I	F	M	B	R	A	I	T	C	Q	A	D	Z	I	T	H	D
O	M	E	V	E	T	E	G	O	O	S	X	L	A	I	E	A	Y
S	A	N	H	A	U	D	C	T	L	E	L	O	E	M	N	G	A
E	S	E	T	A	R	C	O	S	Q	I	E	J	A	H	P	E	B
D	S	I	O	Y	E	B	A	I	E	N	B	M	O	A	C	J	I
E	R	T	D	V	L	A	T	R	S	S	A	T	E	S	A	I	L
M	A	R	C	E	A	P	J	A	A	T	N	A	C	X	E	H	M
I	Y	D	E	D	S	H	A	U	T	E	E	V	F	R	A	S	O
H	O	I	N	Q	L	C	V	E	A	I	O	B	I	G	K	D	K
C	A	B	G	A	M	U	A	S	N	N	A	O	U	A	E	B	A
R	S	K	A	F	E	A	R	R	E	P	I	E	T	O	X	P	M
A	A	Z	H	I	D	L	Z	N	T	A	D	M	A	A	L	T	S
Y	U	A	S	E	M	A	E	J	A	E	P	A	N	I	L	H	X
I	A	I	C	N	I	V	A	D	O	N	S	O	I	U	R	P	I

SOLUTION ON PAGE 210

SPACE RACE

Four intrepid teams of astronauts have set out to explore the solar system.

1. The team that was assigned the task of clearing asteroids did not finish first.

2. Charlie team were led by laid-back Colonel Roger Bucks.

3. The lunar base was completed by Crash Cordon's team; their phonetic alphabet codename comes immediately after the team that came third.

4. James Kerk's team completed his mission earlier than Alpha team who were attempting to land on Mars.

5. The team attempting to create a solar station had the furthest to travel and the riskiest assignment, so they were the last to complete their mission.

Team	Mission	Leader	Completion
Alpha			
Bravo			
Charlie			
Delta			

SOLUTION ON PAGE 211

	Lunar base	Asteroid clearance	Solar station	Mars landing	Crash Cordon	Roger Bucks	James Kerk	Daniel Daring	First	Second	Third	Fourth
Alpha												
Bravo												
Charlie												
Delta												
First												
Second												
Third												
Fourth												
Crash Cordon												
Roger Bucks												
James Kerk												
Daniel Daring												

"I do not think there is any thrill that can go through the human heart like that felt by the inventor as he sees some creation of the brain unfolding to success... such emotions make a man forget food, sleep, friends, love, everything."

NIKOLA TESLA

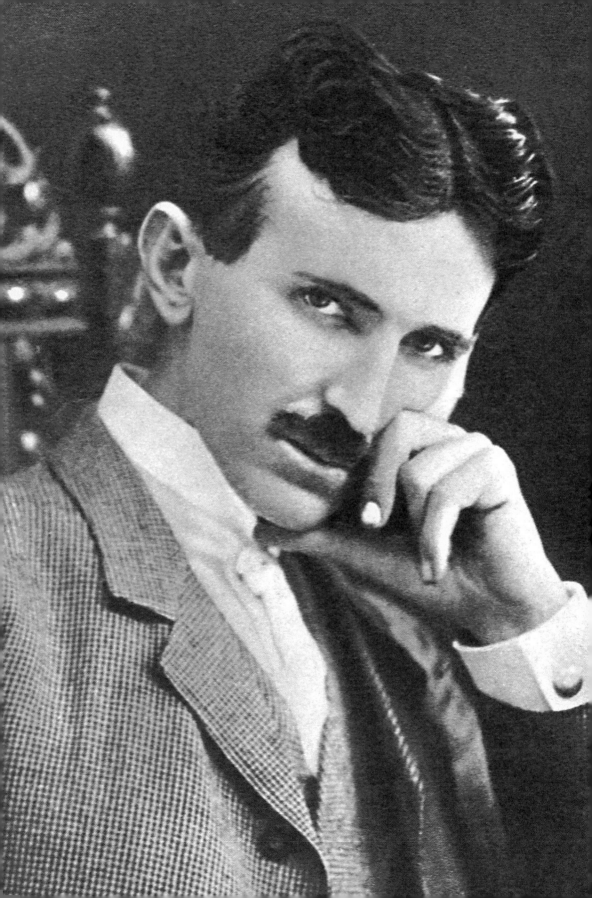

POWER GRID VII

1. Run a single, unbroken wire around the grid that passes through each of the relays to complete the circuit.

2. The wire must enter and leave each square through the centre of one of its four sides.

3. If the wire enters a gold relay, it must immediately turn 90 degrees left or right on that square. It must also pass straight through the square it came from and the square it leads to.

4. If the wire enters a silver relay, it must pass straight through the square. It must also turn left or right in the next and/or preceding square.

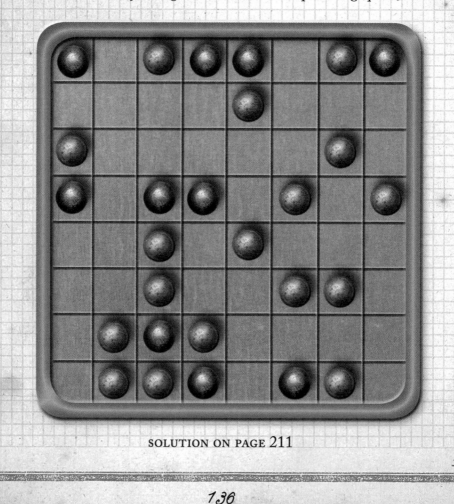

SOLUTION ON PAGE 211

PATTERN RECOGNITION III

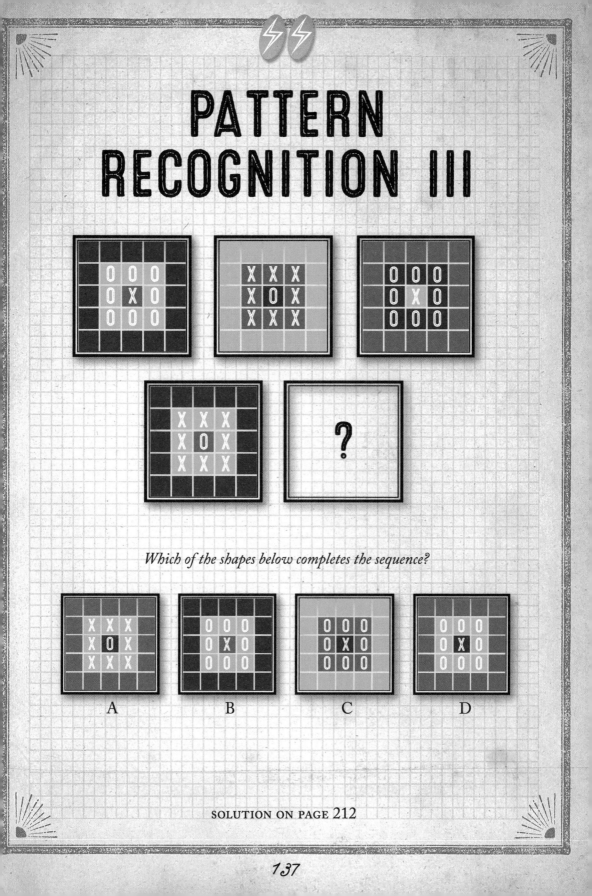

Which of the shapes below completes the sequence?

A

B

C

D

SOLUTION ON PAGE 212

FEATHERED FRIENDS

Tesla could often be seen feeding the pigeons, which he referred to as "my only friends". His fondness for one pigeon in particular bordered on romantic affection.

On the opposite page you can see a variety of birds. Take a couple of minutes to picture them in your mind and then turn over the page…

> "I loved that pigeon as a man loves a woman, and she loved me. As long as I had her, there was a purpose to my life."
>
> **NIKOLA TESLA**

SOLUTION ON PAGE 214

Two of the items above have swapped positions. Can you say which?

COMPLETE THE GRID XVI

What belongs in the empty box?

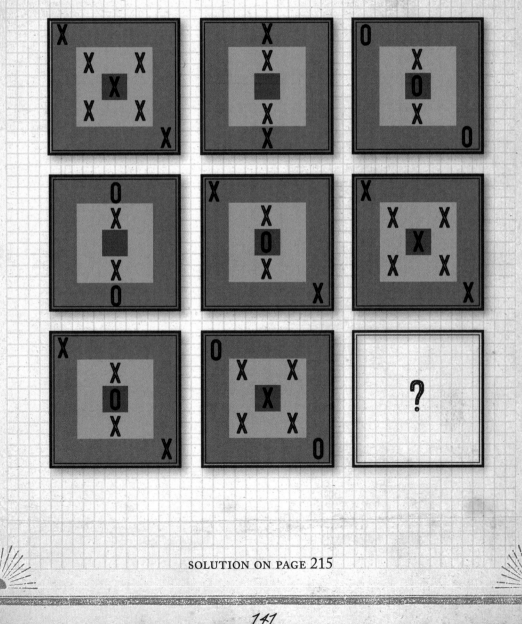

TOWN PLANNING IV

Your city is divided into six districts. The mayor has decreed that each district shall have one of each of the following facilities:

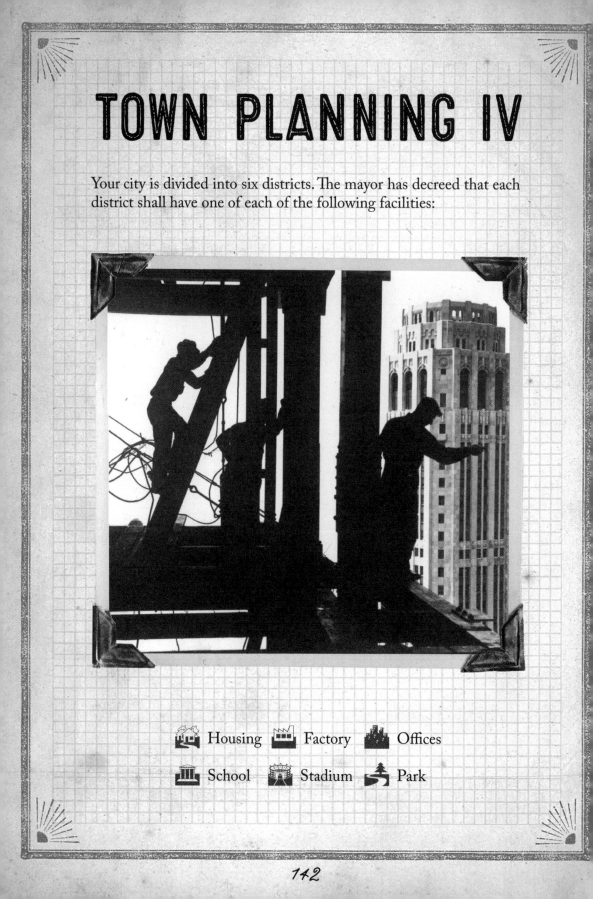

🏘️ Housing 🏭 Factory 🏙️ Offices

🏛️ School 🏟️ Stadium 🌲 Park

You must make sure that there is no more than one of each facility in each column and row, and that no facilities of the same type are adjacent to one another.

SOLUTION ON PAGE 215

VALUE SYSTEM X

Work out the value of each component to determine what number replaces the question mark.

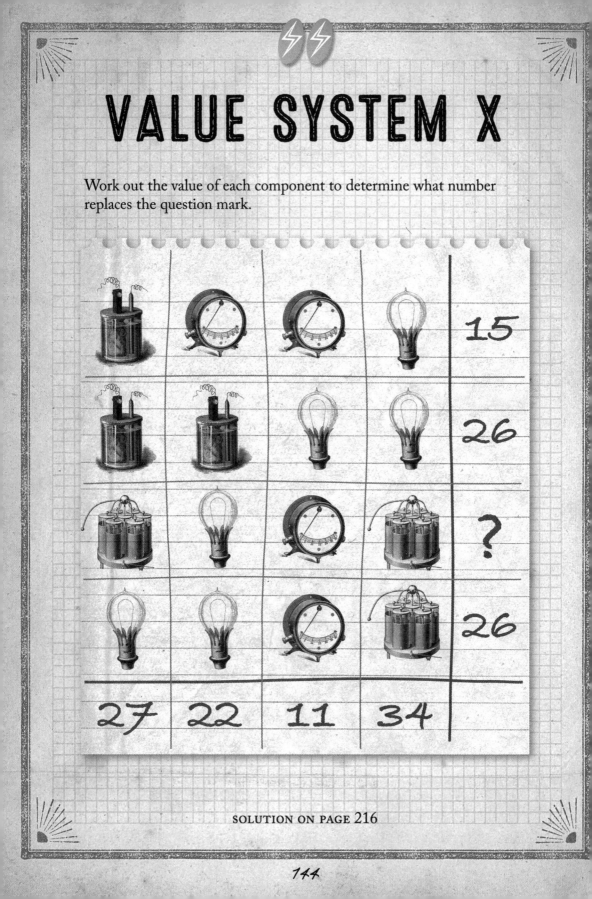

MARK TWAIN

Nikola Tesla was friends with renowned author Mark Twain. Below is a quote from Twain encrypted. Can you decode it?

H	T	N	I	N	G
T	H	E	L	I	G
B	U	G	A	N	D
H	U	N	I	N	G
T	H	E	L	I	G
E	T	W	L	E	N
R	E	D	C	E	B
R	D	I	F	F	E
R	I	T	S	T	H
E	M	A	T	T	E
Y	A	L	A	R	G
S	R	E	A	L	L
T	W	O	R	D	I
H	E	R	I	G	H
R	D	A	N	D	T
I	G	H	T	W	O
L	M	O	S	T	R
E	N	T	H	E	A
E	B	E	T	W	E
F	E	R	T	N	C
T	H	E	D	I	F

SOLUTION ON PAGE 216

POWER SUPPLY ·VII

1. Place a battery (⚡) in a square adjacent to each lightbulb on the grid.

2. Adjacent squares share a side (north, south, east and west) not just a corner.

3. No battery can be placed adjacent to another battery.

4. The numbers tell you how many batteries must be placed in each row or column.

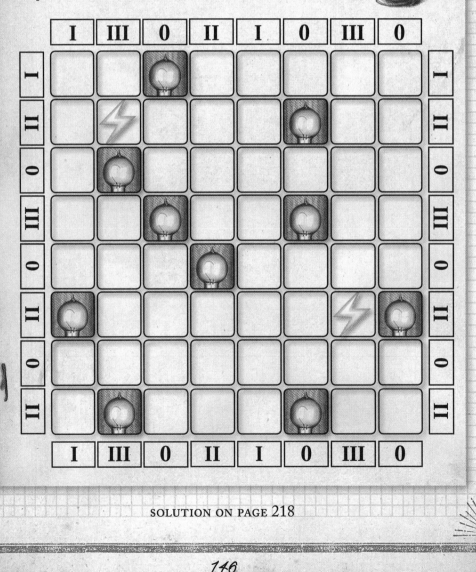

SOLUTION ON PAGE 218

TOWER OF DREAMS

Tesla's new tower was completed. The total value of the project was one million dollars.

The cost of construction was $900,000 more than the cost of the land. So what did Tesla pay for the land?

The real Tesla Tower (Wardenclyffe Tower) was built in 1901. Tesla ultimately intended it to be a means of wireless power transmission but he was unable to find investors and it was abandoned in 1906.

SOLUTION ON PAGE 219

COMPLETE THE GRID XVII

What belongs in the empty box?

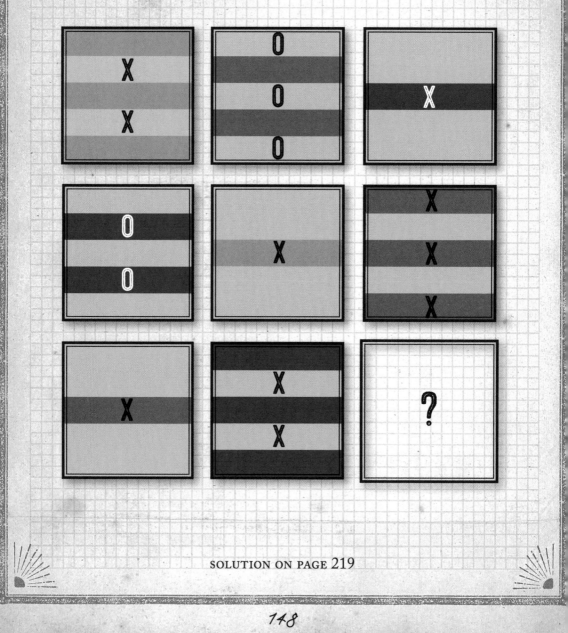

❝ Though we may never be able to comprehend human life, we know certainly that it is a movement, of whatever nature it be. The existence of movement unavoidably implies a body which is being moved and a force which is moving it. Hence, wherever there is life, there is a mass moved by a force. All mass possesses inertia; all force tends to persist. ❞

NIKOLA TESLA

TOWN PLANNING V

Your city is divided into six districts. The mayor has decreed that each district shall have one of each of the following facilities:

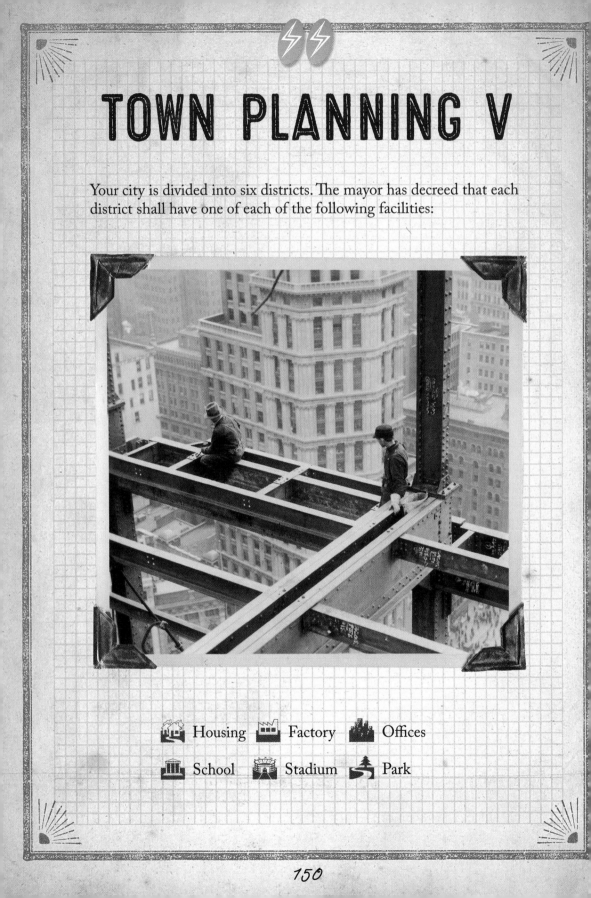

🏘 Housing　🏭 Factory　🏙 Offices

🏛 School　🏟 Stadium　🌲 Park

You must make sure that there is no more than one of each facility in each column and row, and that no facilities of the same type are adjacent to one another.

SOLUTION ON PAGE 220

COMPLETE THE GRID XVIII

What belongs in the empty box?

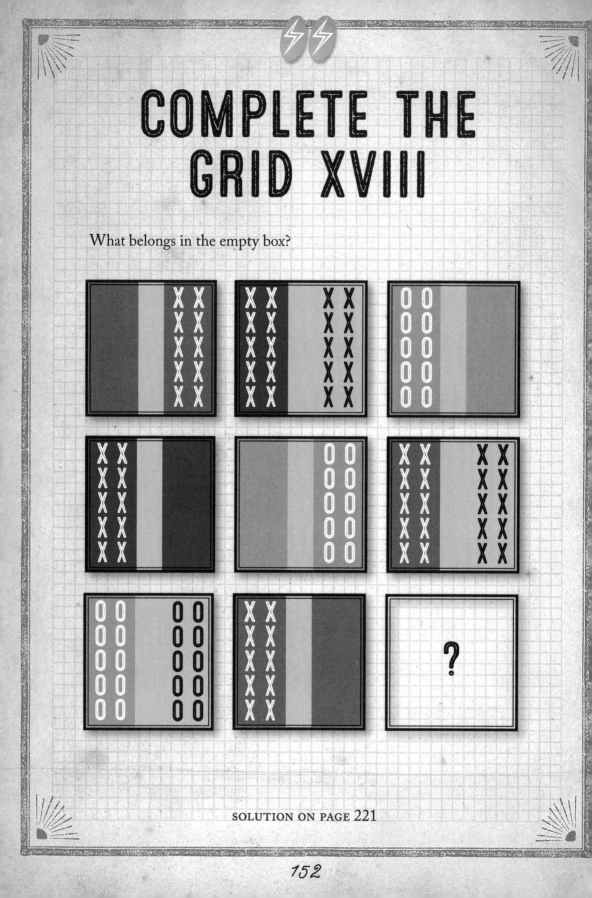

SWING BATTER

Henry was staring through the glass while a group of children played baseball outside his home.

One of the children hit a home run; unfortunately the ball hit the glass and broke it. Henry went outside but the children had started to argue among themselves, oblivious to his distress. A while later they discovered Henry on the ground, dead.

The distraught children called their mother who was clearly annoyed but remained quite calm at the sight of Henry's corpse. After admonishing them, she helped the children to dispose of Henry's body in their back garden.

Was the mother a cold-blooded psychopath?

SOLUTION ON PAGE 221

PATTERN RECOGNITION IV

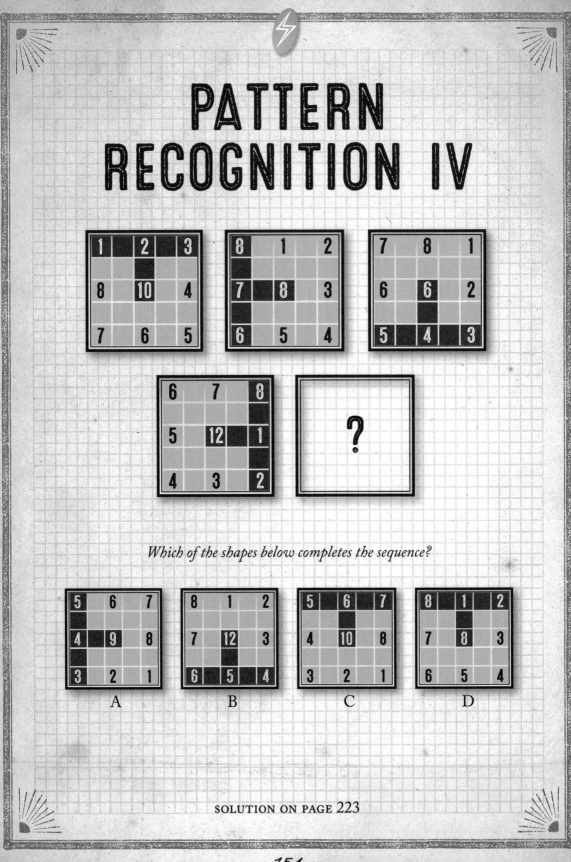

Which of the shapes below completes the sequence?

A
B
C
D

SOLUTION ON PAGE 223

SCIENCE CONFERENCE

A group of eminent scientists meet in Vienna.

All but two of them are biologists.

All but two of them are chemists.

All but two of them are physicists.

How many scientists attend the conference?

SOLUTION ON PAGE 223

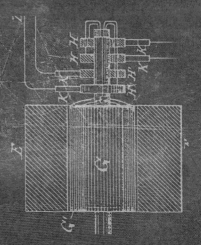

SOLUTIONS

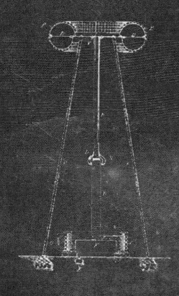

BORN IN A STORM

All of the months have 28 days (including the ones with 30 and 31 days).

COMPLETE THE GRID I

Each row and column contains two gold squares and a total of five rivets.

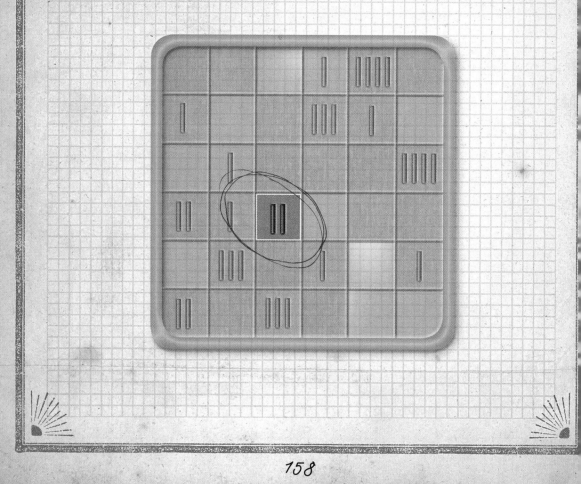

FAITH, HOPE AND CLARITY

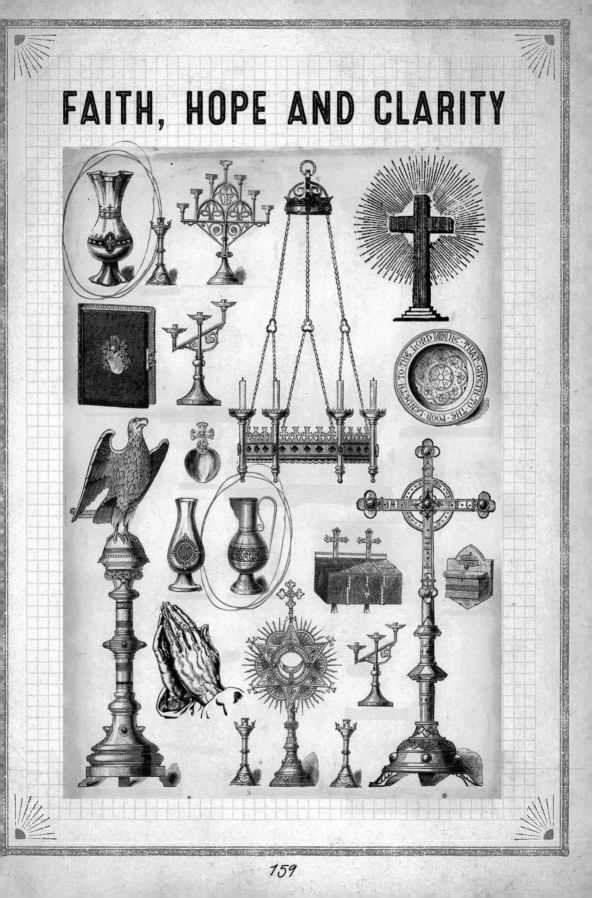

SEQUENCE 1

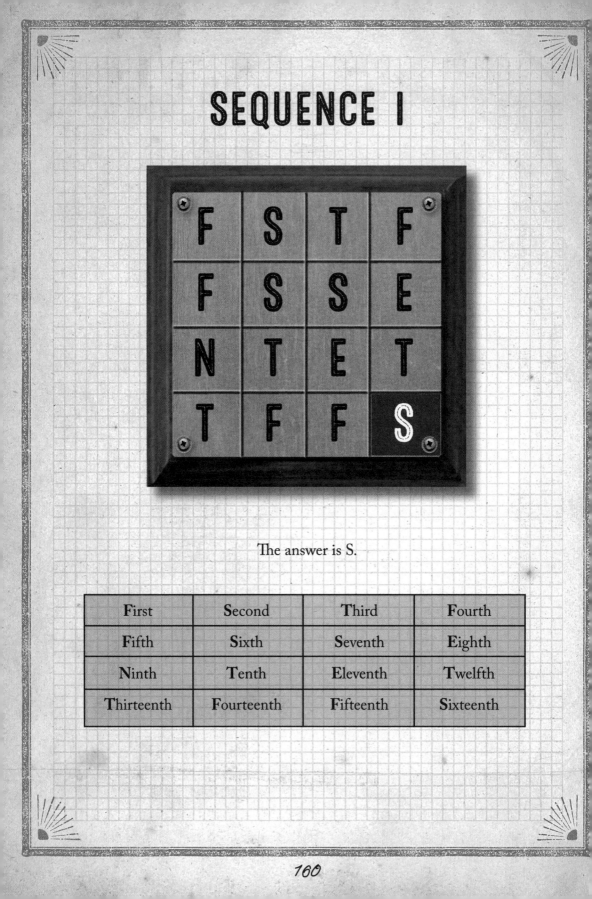

F	S	T	F
F	S	S	E
N	T	E	T
T	F	F	**S**

The answer is S.

First	Second	Third	Fourth
Fifth	Sixth	Seventh	Eighth
Ninth	Tenth	Eleventh	Twelfth
Thirteenth	Fourteenth	Fifteenth	Sixteenth

STONE AGE PIONEERS

	Invention	Inspiration	Reward
Zog	Fire	Hunting	Worshipped
Ugg	Wheel	Mushrooms	Banished
Stig	Plough	Sabre-tooth tiger	Monument
Nigel	Bow	Thunderstorm	Promoted to chief

VALUE SYSTEM I

The missing number is 10.

1   2   3   4

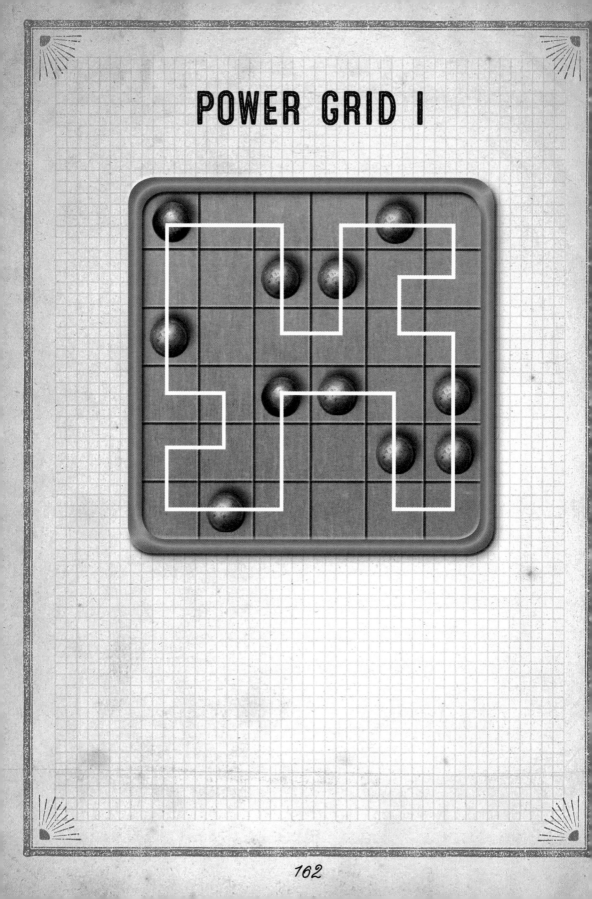

WATERY GRAVE

The water in the three rooms was in different states: liquid, solid and gas. So the man in contact with the ice died of hypothermia and/or suffocation, and the one in the room full of steam perished from burns and dehydration.

COMPLETE THE GRID II

Each row and column contains two silver buttons and one gold button.

VISIONS

PATTERN RECOGNITION I

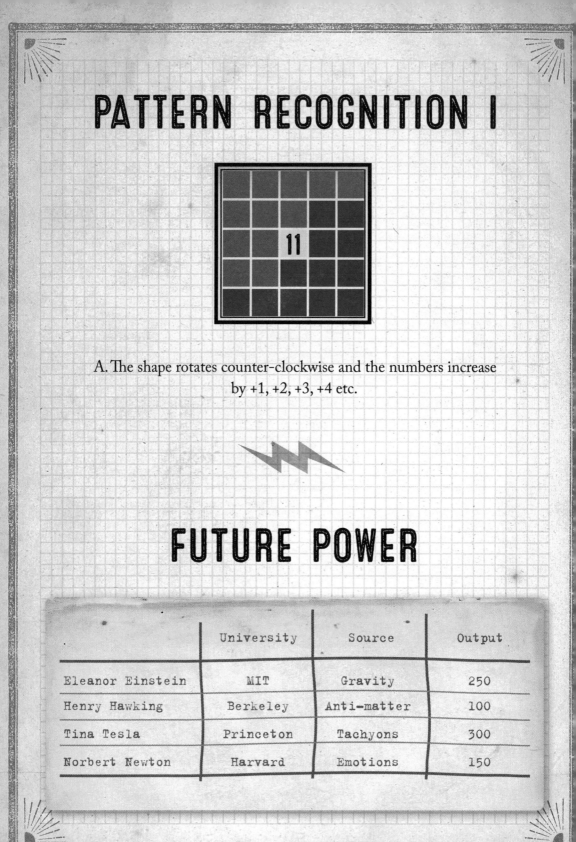

A. The shape rotates counter-clockwise and the numbers increase by +1, +2, +3, +4 etc.

FUTURE POWER

	University	Source	Output
Eleanor Einstein	MIT	Gravity	250
Henry Hawking	Berkeley	Anti-matter	100
Tina Tesla	Princeton	Tachyons	300
Norbert Newton	Harvard	Emotions	150

WATCH YOUR EIGHT

20 times.

8	18	28	38	48	58	68	78	80	81
82	83	84	85	86	87	88	89	98	

COMPLETE THE GRID III

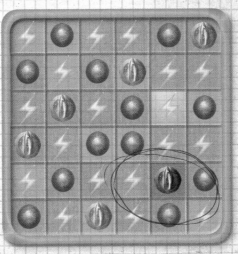

Each row and column contains two brass squares and three electrical discharges, two domes and one switch.

FAMILIARITY

Sir Avery had three daughters: identical triplets, one of whom was raised by his ex-wife. Clara and Betty recognized the familiar features of their long-lost sister and were upset that their portion of the will would have to be split three ways.

VALUE SYSTEM II

The missing number is 12.

5   4   2   3

SEQUENCE 11

The answer is 8. The sequence relates to the number of letters in the name of each month.

January	Februray	March	April
May	June	July	August
September	October	November	December

POWER GRID II

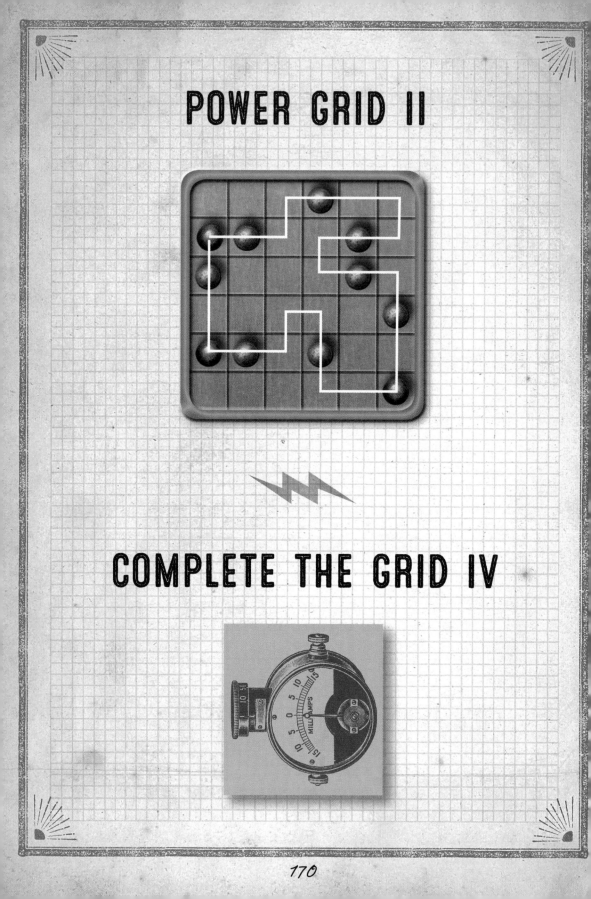

COMPLETE THE GRID IV

VALUE SYSTEM III

The missing number is 13.

7   1   3   5

"Life is and will ever remain an equation incapable of solution, but it contains certain known factors."

NIKOLA TESLA

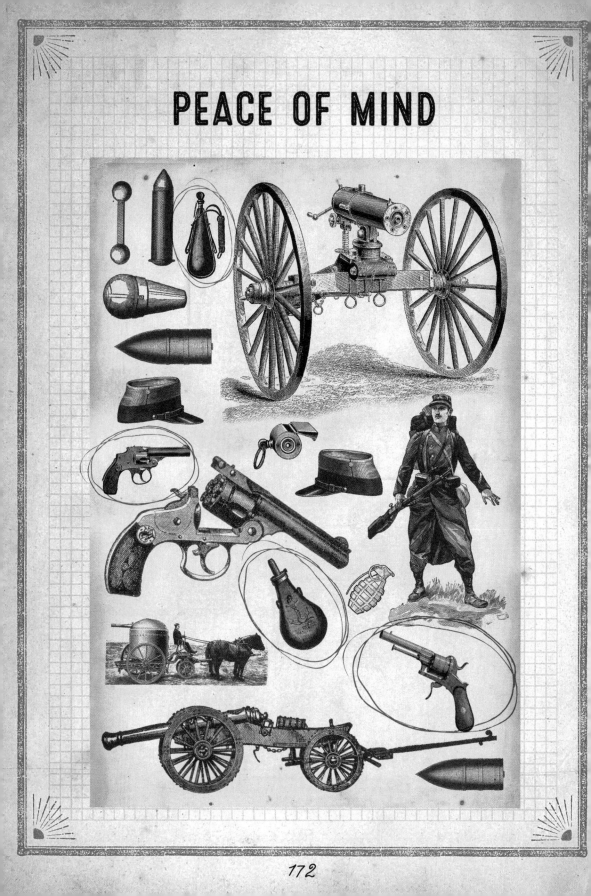

FILL IN YOUR NAME

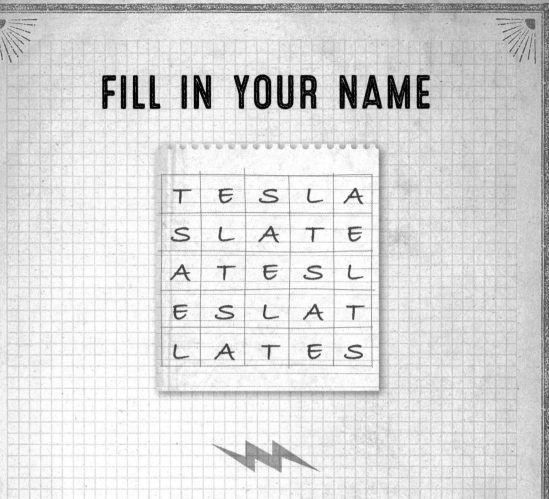

T	E	S	L	A
S	L	A	T	E
A	T	E	S	L
E	S	L	A	T
L	A	T	E	S

IT'S ALIVE!

Professor	Location	Golem	Outcome
Van der Volt	New York	Bob	Bloody rampage
Bankenstein	Paris	Jerry	Got married
Knutz	Berlin	Ron	National hero
Phreekdoubt	London	Phil	Therapy

THE $50,000 JOKE

The two men were staying at the same hotel in adjoining rooms.
Edison's snoring had been keeping Tesla awake.

For many years Tesla lived in room 3327 of the New Yorker Hotel.

COMPLETE THE GRID V

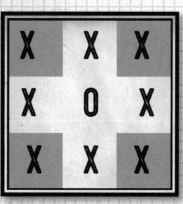

POWER SUPPLY I

IMPOSTER

Hardy had done her homework and discovered that Doctor Jefferson had a pathological fear of needles.

VALUE SYSTEM IV

The missing number is 22.

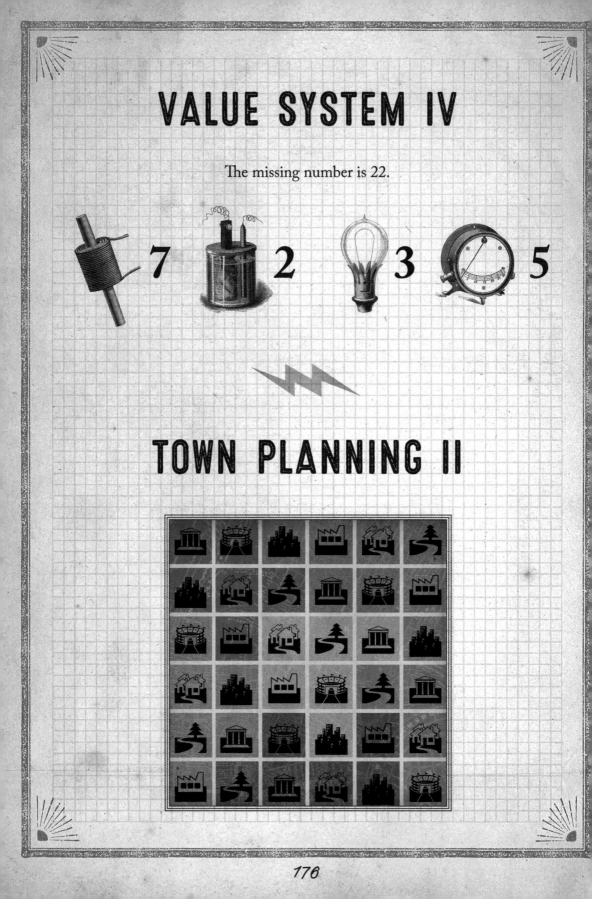

7   2   3   5

TOWN PLANNING II

POWER GRID III

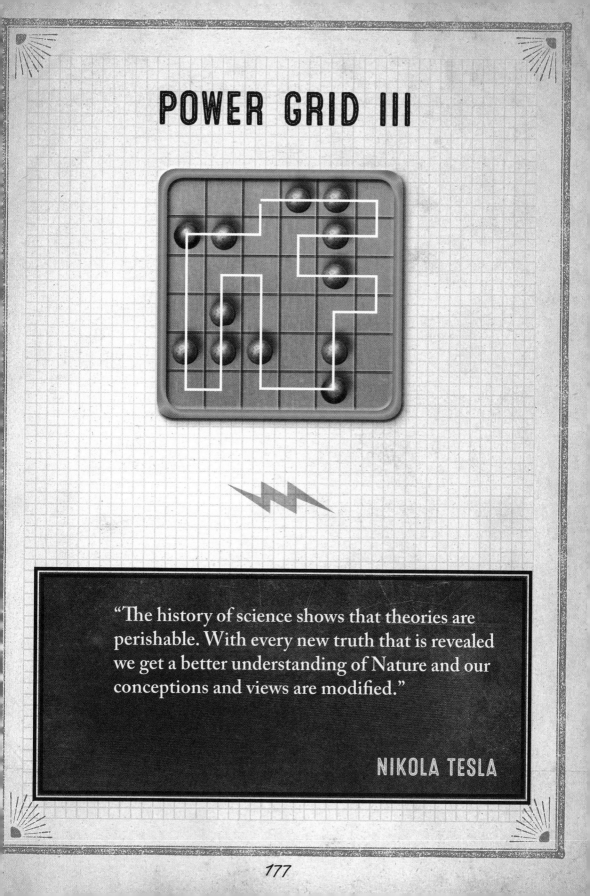

"The history of science shows that theories are perishable. With every new truth that is revealed we get a better understanding of Nature and our conceptions and views are modified."

NIKOLA TESLA

LOST IN THE GRID

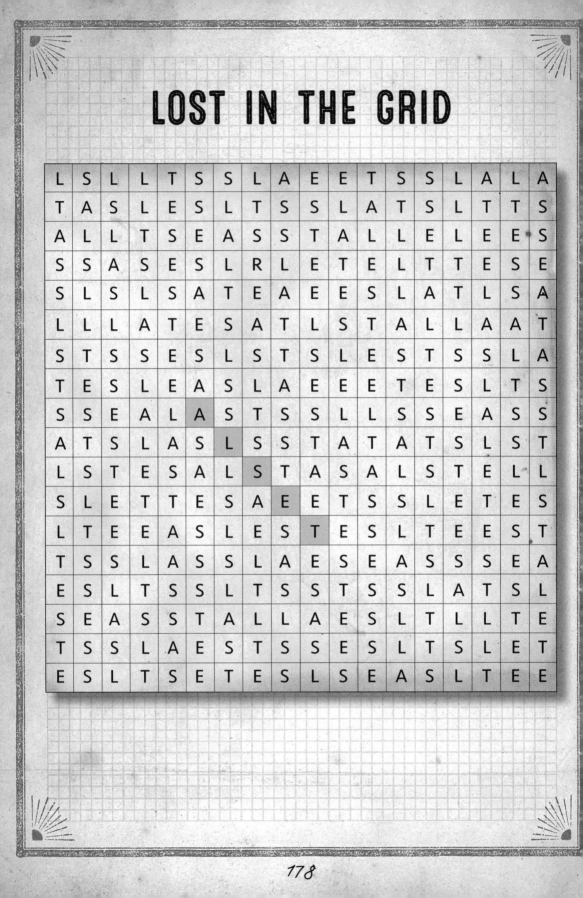

COMPLETE THE GRID VI

FREQUENCY 1

1: Isaac Newton
2: Albert Einstein
3: Michael Faraday
4: Nikola Tesla

POWER SUPPLY II

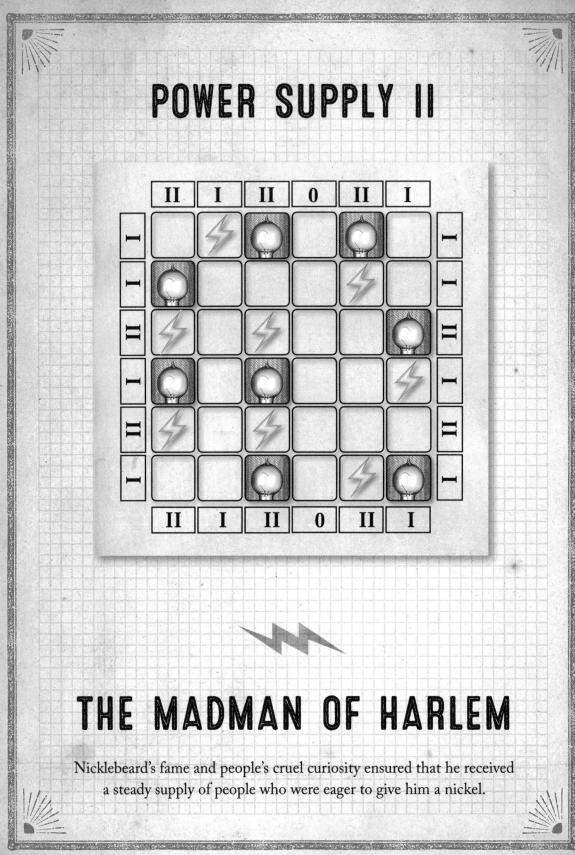

THE MADMAN OF HARLEM

Nicklebeard's fame and people's cruel curiosity ensured that he received a steady supply of people who were eager to give him a nickel.

VIVE LA FRANCE

SMUGGLERS

The gang was smuggling stolen vehicles into the country.

SCIENCE VS CATASTROPHE

Professor	Field	Catastrophe	Solution
Dick Dorkins	Astrophysics	Global flood	Move to Mars
Ty Neilson	Marine Biology	Meteor strike	Live underground
Harry Stottle	Geology	Alien invasion	Genetic mutation
Gary Leo	Paleontology	Ice Age	Robot servants

POWER GRID IV

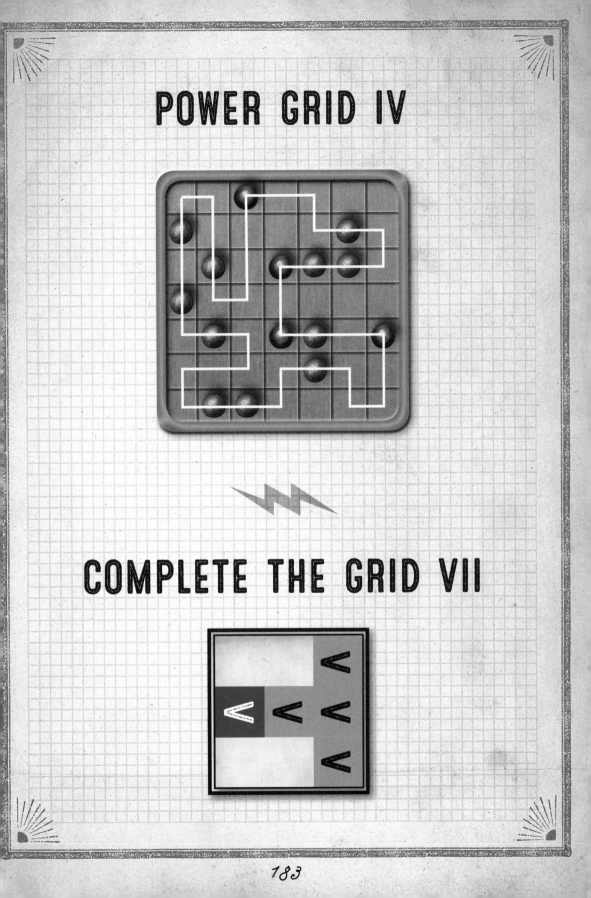

COMPLETE THE GRID VII

VALUE SYSTEM V

The missing number is 22.

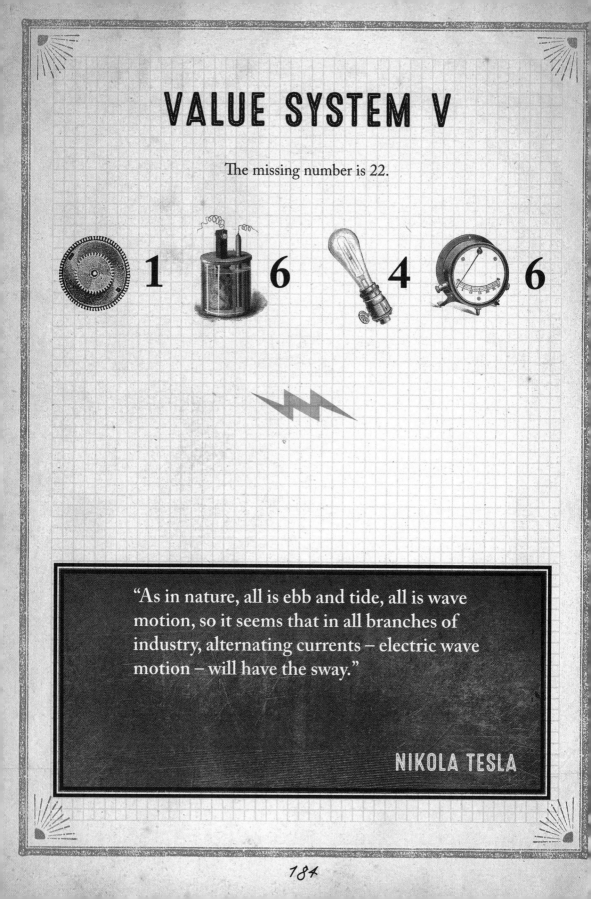

1   6   4   6

"As in nature, all is ebb and tide, all is wave motion, so it seems that in all branches of industry, alternating currents – electric wave motion – will have the sway."

NIKOLA TESLA

POWER SUPPLY III

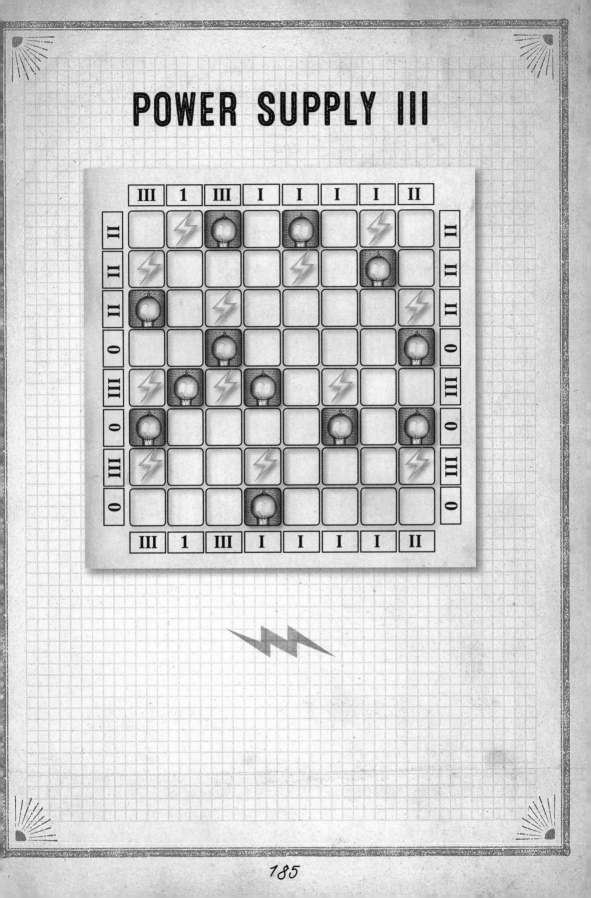

RESEARCH

Only accountants can claim to be statisticians because real statisticians have to pretend to be something else and biochemists cannot lie.
So Team 2 is Alpha Team.

Alpha (2)

6 accountants changing the truth so they now become **6 statisticians**

The biochemists cannot pretend to be anything other than what they are and we know that some must be present in Charlie Team, which means Charlie Team is Team 1.

Charlie (1)

2 biochemists   truthfully claiming to be biochemists

2 statisticians   falsely claiming to be biochemists

2 accountants   changing the truth so they now become biochemists

So that leaves us with Bravo Team as Team 3 which must consist of statisticians and accountants.

Bravo (3)

3 statisticians   falsely claiming to be accountants

3 accountants   truthfully claiming to be accountants

So 11 lying statisticians are sent home!

HANDY

A man with a pocket watch. Two of his hands were on the ends of his arms and the remaining three were on the watch.

BAGELS

First determine how many bagels the seller started with by working backwards (adding two bagels and doubling the result) for each gang.

After the third gang	1 bagel	+2 x2 = 6 bagels
After the second gang	6 bagels	+2 x2 = 16 bagels
After the first gang	16 bagels	+2 x2 = 36 bagels

Multiplying the 36 bagels by $0.02 gives $0.72 which the seller pays each day.

So the bagel seller makes a daily profit (from his single bagel sale at $1.50) of $0.78, just enough to buy his next consignment and pocketing a meagre six cents.

COMPLETE THE GRID VIII

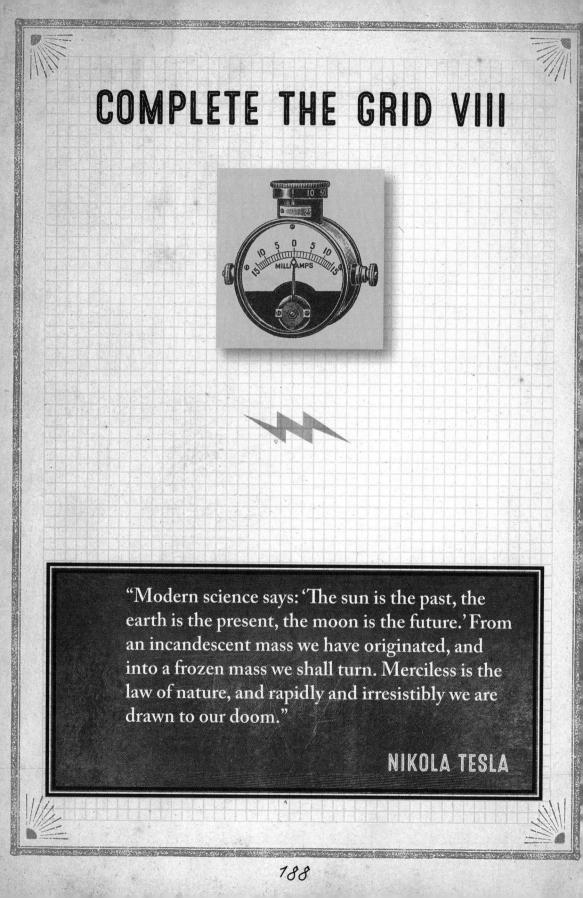

"Modern science says: 'The sun is the past, the earth is the present, the moon is the future.' From an incandescent mass we have originated, and into a frozen mass we shall turn. Merciless is the law of nature, and rapidly and irresistibly we are drawn to our doom."

NIKOLA TESLA

NEW WORLD

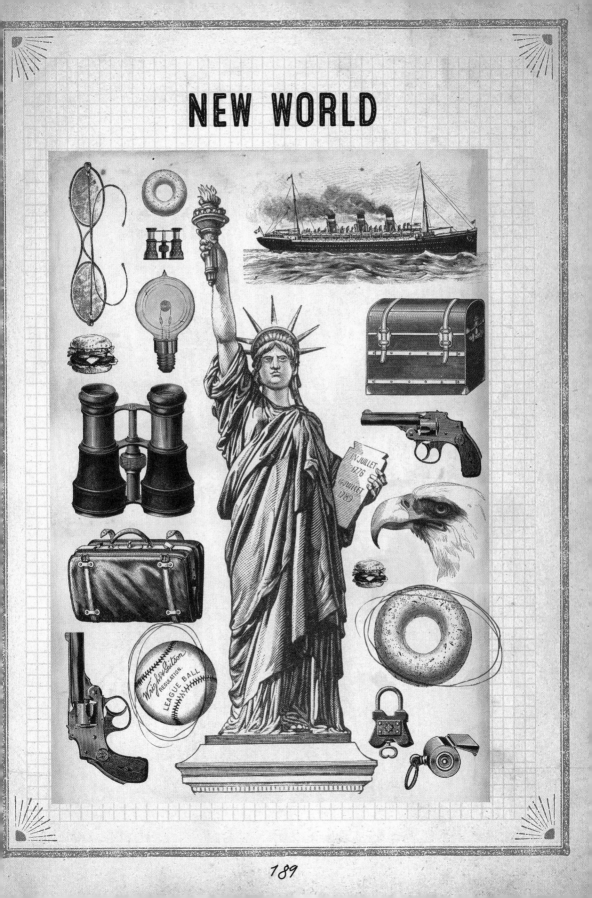

DEATH DEALERS

Buyer	Target	Motive	Bid
Mafia	The Eiffel Tower	Vendetta	$100 million
Yakuza	The White House	Blackmail	$250 million
Triads	Big Ben	Power	$901 million
Cartels	Sistine Chapel	Fun	$666 million

COMPLETE THE GRID IX

```
O   O   O

O   X   O

O   O   O
```

SEQUENCE III

101. The numbers on the bottom row are the Base 3 (ternary) equivalents of the decimal numbers on the top row.

One	Two	Three	Four	Five
1	2	10	11	12
Six	Seven	Eight	Nine	Ten
20	21	22	100	**101**

VALUE SYSTEM VI

The missing number is 19.

8   4   3   7

POWER SUPPLY IV

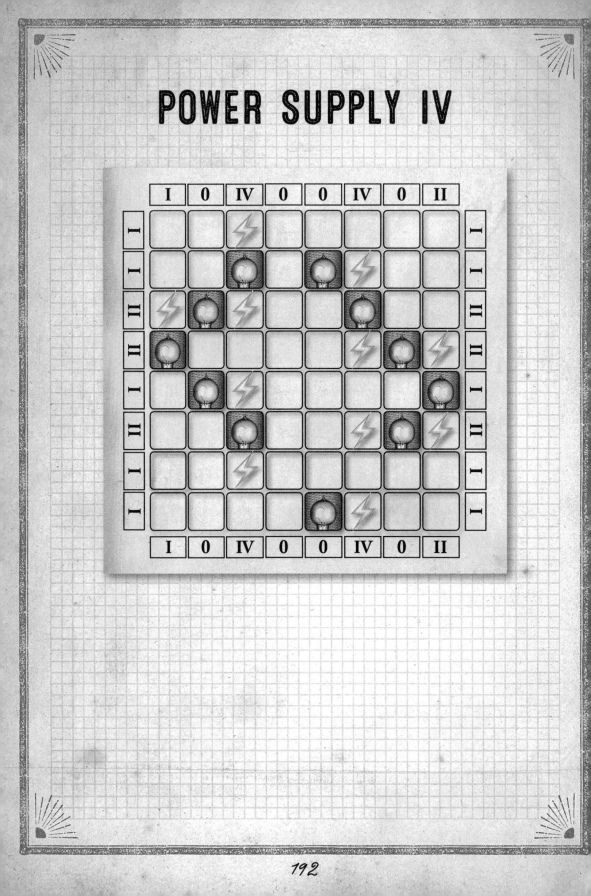

MARATHON

None. You might have been tempted to say 'bronze' if you made the mistake of thinking that overtaking the second place runner would put Jack in first place; in fact Jack would replace that runner in second place and would pushed back to forth by the other two runners.

POWER GRID V

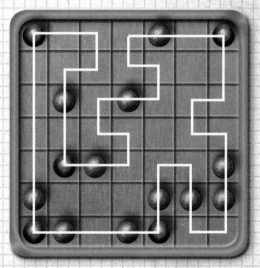

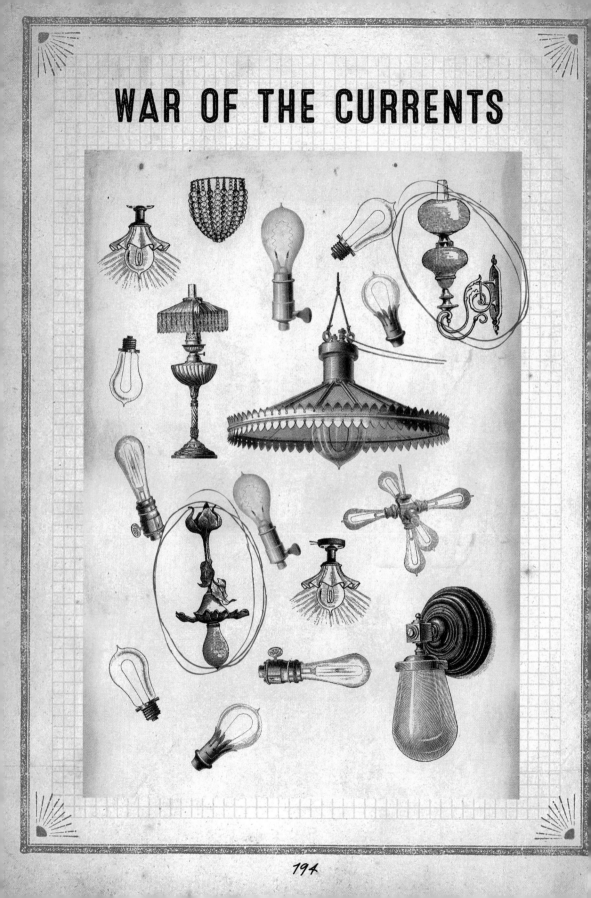

POWER SUPPLY V

MULTIDISCIPLINARY

	GROHL	HENDRIX	DICKINSON
CHEMISTRY		✓	✓
GEOLOGY	✓	✓	
ZOOLOGY	✓		✓
MATHEMATICS	✓	✓	
PSYCHOLOGY	✓		✓
ASTRONOMY		✓	✓

COMPLETE THE GRID X

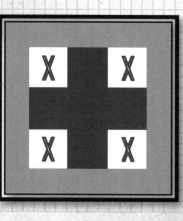

VALUE SYSTEM VII

The missing number is 26.

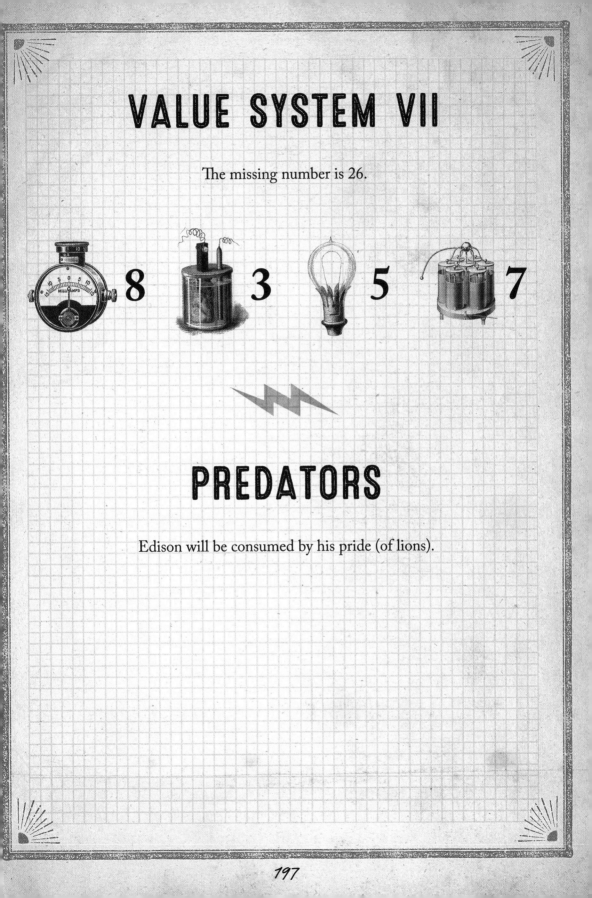

8 3 5 7

PREDATORS

Edison will be consumed by his pride (of lions).

PATTERN RECOGNITION II

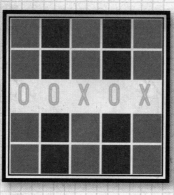

D. The two inner bars are the same colour as the preceding outer bars; the three outer bars are the same colour as the preceding symbols; and the symbols are the same colour as the preceding inner bars. The symbols are the number sequence 1, 2, 3, 4 in binary.

TELEFORCE

Tower B has the faster rate of fire. The important factor here is the interval between firings.

Tower A: There are 4 intervals between the first and fifth shot; dividing intervals by the time taken gives 1.25 seconds per interval.

Tower B: There are 9 intervals between the first and tenth shot; dividing intervals by the time taken gives 1.11 seconds per interval.

Tower A will take 13.75 seconds to fire 12 shots (11 intervals) whereas **Tower B** will take 12.21 seconds.

COMPLETE THE GRID XI

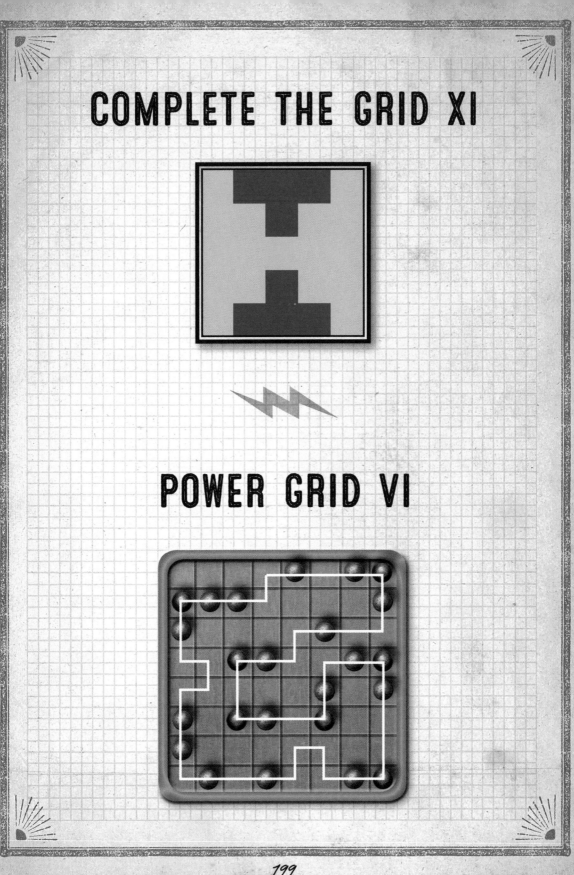

POWER GRID VI

FREQUENCY II

1. Leonardo Da Vinci
2. Benjamin Franklin
3. Thomas Edison
4. Blaise Pascal

ELECTRIC CITY

Prize	City	Mayor	Innovation
First	Jackson	Horan	Spaceport
Second	Boston	Payne	Zero G arena
Third	Miami	Styles	Undersea dome
Fourth	Seattle	Tomlinson	Weather control

COMPLETE THE GRID XII

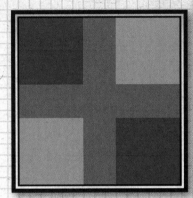

FACING FACTS

Alice concludes that everyone was laughing because, like her, they initially believed they hadn't been affected. If Bertha believed this and saw that Alice's face was unaffected, Carly's laughter would make no sense; Bertha would then conclude that Carly was laughing at her and she would stop laughing herself. Since Bertha hadn't stopped laughing she must have concluded that Carly is laughing at Alice.

VALUE SYSTEM VIII

4 7 9 5

BREAK IN

The two men were firefighters. Sadly, a fire really did destroy Tesla's Fifth Avenue laboratory in 1895.

TOWN PLANNING III

WATT DID THEY SAY?

Alfred's first statement was incorrect. He generated 4000 watts.
Bart's last statement was incorrect. He generated 4800 watts.
Charlie's second statement was incorrect. He generated 3600 watts.

COMPLETE THE GRID XIII

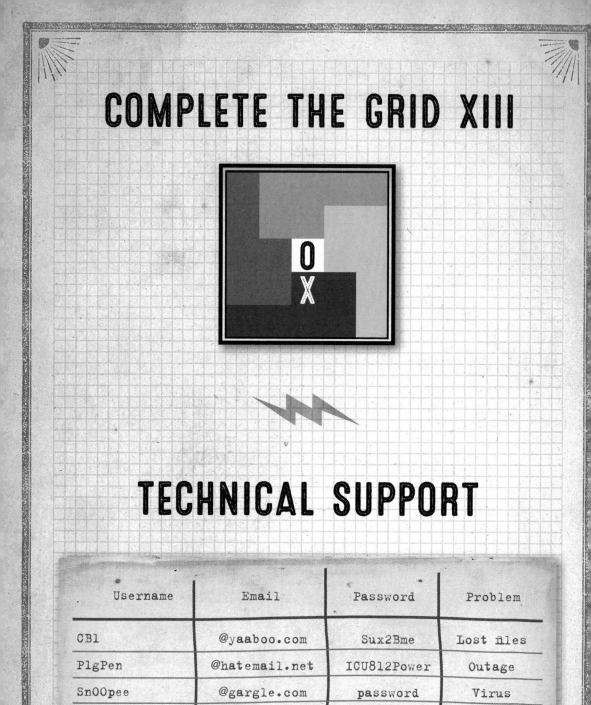

TECHNICAL SUPPORT

Username	Email	Password	Problem
CB1	@yaaboo.com	Sux2Bme	Lost files
PlgPen	@hatemail.net	ICU812Power	Outage
Sn00pee	@gargle.com	password	Virus
W00dstck	@ickypedia.org	12345	No network

LIFE FORCE

SHOPPING

Tesla was buying Roman numerals for an analogue clock.
Each line cost $5.

I $5
V $10
VI $15
XII $20

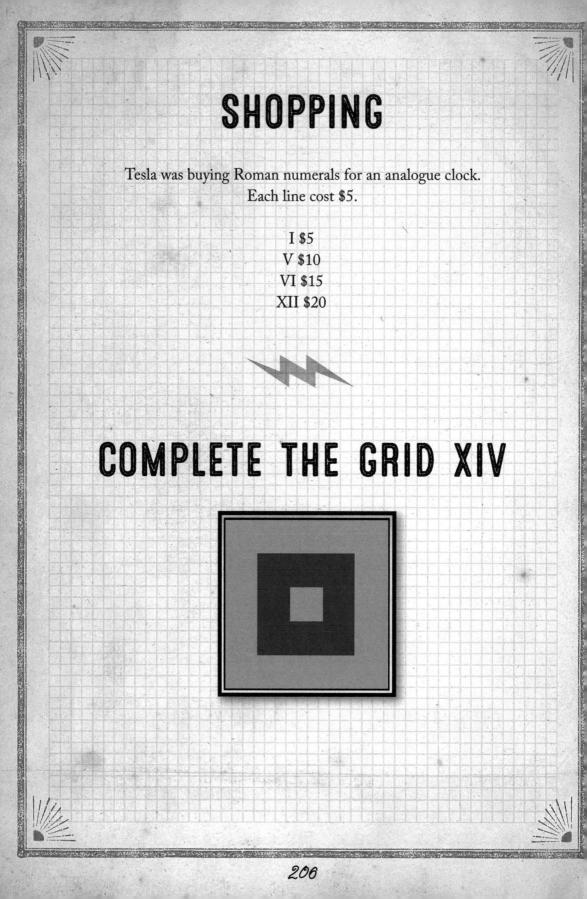

COMPLETE THE GRID XIV

VALUE SYSTEM IX

The missing number is 28.

6 5 8 9

HARDWIRE

Tesla must make a minimum of two trips downstairs.
Tesla goes down to the basement where the three wires are labelled.
He connects wire A to wire B then goes back upstairs. He attaches
pairs of wires to his machine (there are three possible combinations)
until he finds the one that makes a circuit. The other wire is therefore
'C' so he attaches the appropriate label to it. Then he connects the
newly labelled 'C' wire to one of the other wires which he labels
'A' and the remaining wire 'B'.

Going back to the basement he attaches wire 'A' to wire 'C'.
If it shows a current, all the wires are correct. Otherwise he
swaps over the labels 'A' and 'B', and the job is good.

COMPLETE THE GRID XV

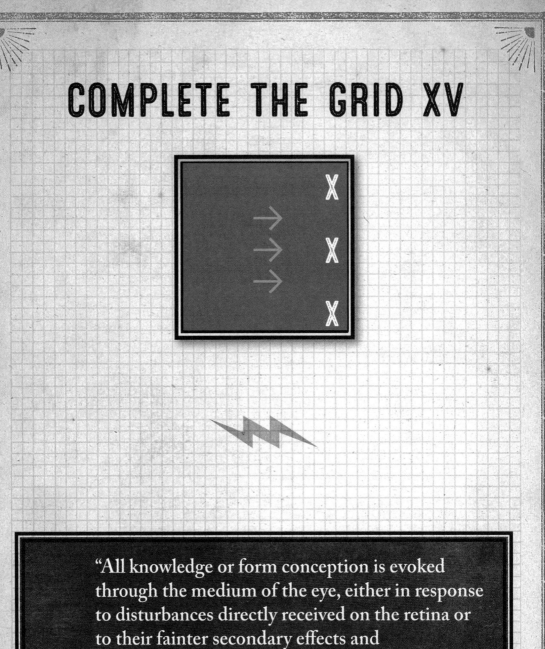

"All knowledge or form conception is evoked
through the medium of the eye, either in response
to disturbances directly received on the retina or
to their fainter secondary effects and
reverberations. Other sense organs can only call
forth feelings which have no reality of existence
and of which no conception can be formed."

NIKOLA TESLA

POWER SUPPLY VI

HIDDEN GENIUS

There are 14 great thinkers in the grid:

N	I	E	T	S	N	E	G	T	T	I	W	A	L	O	A	G	A
O	C	A	O	A	E	K	A	D	I	P	U	I	M	Y	V	O	A
R	I	T	Z	I	C	N	M	I	J	E	H	F	A	G	G	Y	S
A	Y	B	W	D	E	Y	A	W	A	C	E	V	U	S	A	A	R
W	S	A	P	G	E	A	L	S	E	T	K	A	Z	E	L	C	D
D	I	N	A	C	A	O	O	I	A	O	G	A	D	F	I	G	E
A	Q	E	S	A	V	H	L	Z	E	N	E	L	E	A	L	O	T
A	T	C	C	O	B	J	Z	E	E	L	C	Q	S	F	E	E	D
S	R	A	A	K	O	C	A	E	G	T	V	U	Y	A	O	U	A
A	G	Z	L	O	H	H	P	L	W	N	U	O	R	S	O	E	R
V	I	F	M	B	R	A	I	T	C	Q	A	D	Z	I	T	H	D
O	M	E	V	E	T	E	G	O	O	S	X	L	A	I	E	A	Y
S	A	N	H	A	U	D	C	T	L	E	L	O	E	M	N	G	A
E	S	E	T	A	R	C	O	S	Q	I	E	J	A	H	P	E	B
D	S	I	O	Y	E	B	A	I	E	N	B	M	O	A	C	J	I
E	R	T	D	V	L	A	T	R	S	S	A	T	E	S	A	I	L
M	A	R	C	E	A	P	J	A	A	T	N	A	C	X	E	H	M
I	Y	D	E	D	S	H	A	U	T	E	E	V	F	R	A	S	O
H	O	I	N	Q	L	C	V	E	A	I	O	B	I	G	K	D	K
C	A	B	G	A	M	U	A	S	N	N	A	O	U	A	E	B	A
R	S	K	A	F	E	A	R	R	E	P	I	E	T	O	X	P	M
A	A	Z	H	I	D	L	Z	N	T	A	D	M	A	A	L	T	S
Y	U	A	S	E	M	A	E	J	A	E	P	A	N	I	L	H	X
I	A	I	C	N	I	V	A	D	O	N	S	O	I	U	R	P	I

(Ludwig) WITTGENSTEIN, (Blaise) PASCAL, GALILEO, (Nikola) TESLA, (Niels) BOHR MICHELANGELO, ARCHIMEDES, (Marie) CURIE, (Albert) EINSTEIN, ARISTOTLE, (René) DESCARTES, SOCRATES, PLATO, (Leonardo) DAVINCI

SPACE RACE

Team	Mission	Leader	Completion
Alpha	Mars landing	Daniel Daring	Third
Bravo	Lunar base	Crash Cordon	First
Charlie	Solar station	Roger Bucks	Fourth
Delta	Asteroid clearence	James Kerk	Second

POWER GRID VII

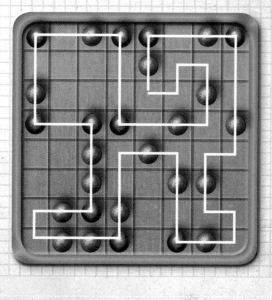

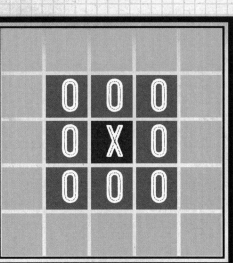

C. The interior patterns alternate. The inner tier is the same colour as the preceding outer tier; the middle tier is the same colour as the preceding inner tier; and the outer tier is the same colour as the preceding middle tier.

> " A single ray of light from a distant star falling upon the eye of a tyrant in bygone times may have altered the course of his life, may have changed the destiny of nations, may have transformed the surface of the globe, so intricate, so inconceivably complex are the processes in Nature. "

NIKOLA TESLA

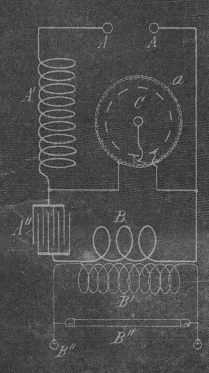

FEATHERED FRIENDS

COMPLETE THE GRID XVI

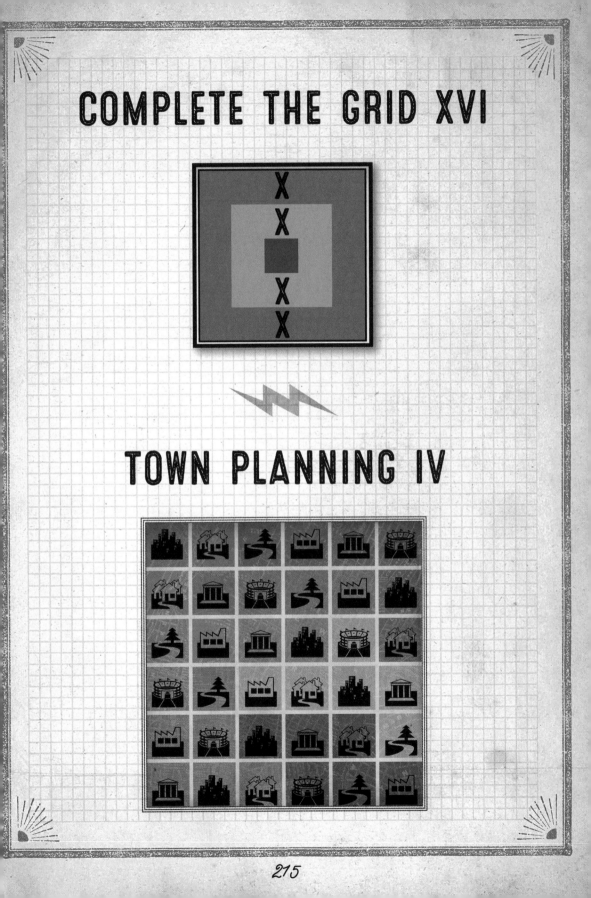

TOWN PLANNING IV

VALUE SYSTEM X

The missing number is 27.

1   5   8   9

MARK TWAIN

The quote has been stripped of spaces and punctuation and broken into blocks of six letters, then the blocks have been reordered back to front.

"The difference between the almost right word and the right word is really a large matter – it's the difference between the lightning-bug and the lightning"

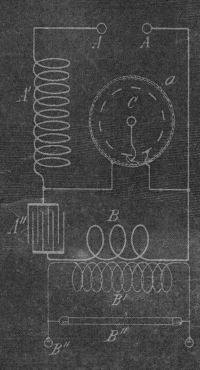

"Everyone should consider his body as a priceless gift from one whom he loves above all, a marvelous work of art, of indescribable beauty, and mystery beyond human conception, and so delicate that a word, a breath, a look, nay, a thought may injure it."

NIKOLA TESLA

POWER SUPPLY VII

TOWER OF DREAMS

If you don't think about the question properly, you might answer $100,000,
but that would take the cost of construction alone up to $1,000,000,
making the total cost $1,100,000. The correct answer is $50,000.

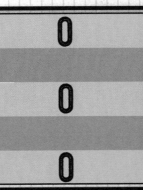

COMPLETE THE GRID XVII

TOWN PLANNING V

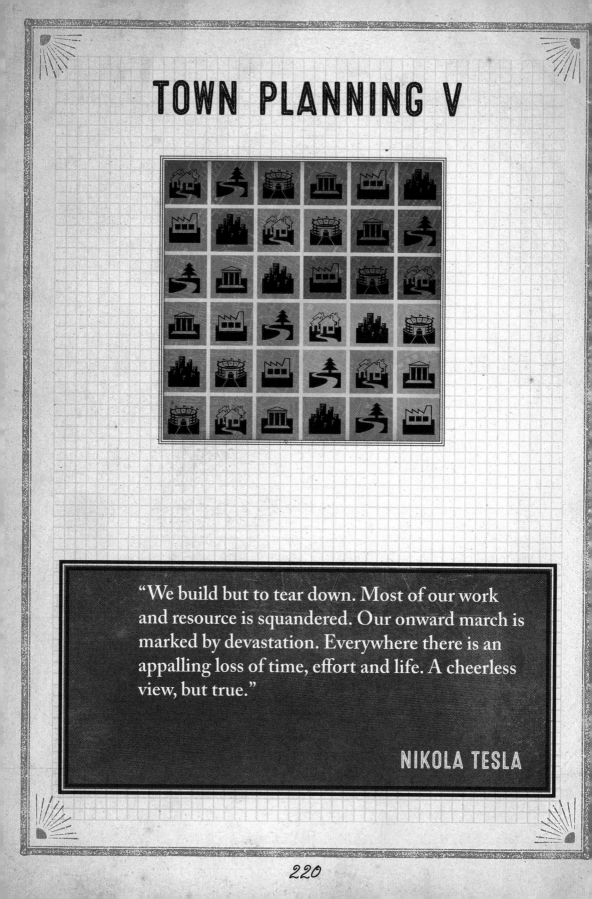

"We build but to tear down. Most of our work and resource is squandered. Our onward march is marked by devastation. Everywhere there is an appalling loss of time, effort and life. A cheerless view, but true."

NIKOLA TESLA

COMPLETE THE GRID XVIII

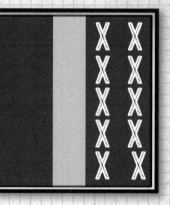

SWING BATTER

No. Henry was the children's pet goldfish.
Playing baseball indoors is not a good idea.

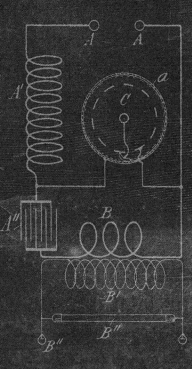

" That is the trouble with many inventors; they lack patience. They lack the willingness to work a thing out slowly and clearly and sharply in their mind, so that they can actually 'feel it work.' They want to try their first idea right off; and the result is they use up lots of money and lots of good material, only to find eventually that they are working in the wrong direction. We all make mistakes, and it is better to make them before we begin. "

NIKOLA TESLA

PATTERN RECOGNITION IV

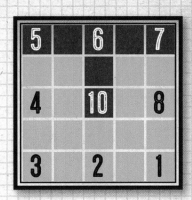

C. The numbers rotate clockwise. The centre number is the sum of the top right and bottom left corners. The T-shape rotates counter-clockwise.

SCIENCE CONFERENCE

Just three scientists.

"What the result of these investigations will be the future will tell; but whatever they may be, and to whatever this principle may lead, I shall be sufficiently recompensed if later it will be admitted that I have contributed a share, however small, to the advancement of science."

NIKOLA TESLA